SIGANA

A
Timeless
MASTERPIECE OF
LOVE

Series I

DANIEL ADONGO

Table of Contents

"Great grandpa! Grandpa! Great grandpa! Wake up! Wake up! Wake up please! Please! Pleaaase? Grandpa wake up! It's morning! We wanna have breakfast with you!" chorused a bunch of high-spirited children teeming with great energy rushing through their veins.

The energy with which these children carried themselves, reminded the chief of a veracious crocodile darting with its half-dead prey from the shores of a lake to the very interiors of its habitat, **where it would secure it amidst a confident group of water reeds only to return a few days later to delight on the meal with great relish.**

Chief Leinad Ongoda, the great grandpa, was never a morning person ever since he could remember. In as much as he understood the immense benefits that a man could attract through hard work and discipline as well as the moral principle of waking up in the morning, he did not believe his parents and fore-fathers teachings that one had to rise up early at the crack of dawn in order to be productive and prosperous in life.

Chief Ongoda discovered in his formative years that he was most productive in the afternoons through the night and would snore away the wee hours of the morning through dawn; And, he had very few memories of sunrise because he hardly ever saw it.

However, Chief was never rebellious to his parents because through formal education and observation, he found out that the world was rapidly changing and the challenges of his parents' time, may have been different from those of his time; and also a generation gap had something to do with it.

Even if this was not the case, Chief Ongoda, a strong believer of virtues and even famed by many of his contemporaries as a virtuoso, constantly practiced the moral teachings of his ancestors passed down from generation to generation through "*ngeche*" (proverbs) and other wise sayings, "*sigana*" (fable stories), riddles, poems, songs and a host of other forms of oral literature.

One of the wise sayings that influenced Chief Ongoda's non-rebellious nature is the one that taught that, "What an old man sees, a young person may not be able to see even if he climbs on top of a tree."

Chief therefore believed that even though he did not totally agree with some of his parents and other elders' sentiments, there must have been some unique wisdom in their words that he was unable to decipher at that time due to his tender age; Hence, he always looked up to his elders as a great source of wisdom, a library of many books in few brains, a gemstone whose treasures could be tapped just by listening and assimilating their words which in many cases required a great deal of patience, humility and diligence.

But this morning was very unique to Chief Ongoda and he had nothing to loose at all but to gain. Chief had lived for over a century and was still going strong and looked only a fraction of his age. This was a rare occurrence in the planet of **Lit-gi-mit** that Chief lived in, in the wide expanse of the solar system that they belonged to.

He had also lived to see his children, grandchildren and even great grandchildren which was another blessing in the world of Lit-gi-mit.

Being woken up by the voices of an assorted mixture of grandchildren and great grandchildren was like being woken up by the chirping of the proverbial *"hera"* (Love) birds who were believed to be the only animals whose sound could elicit instant and long-lasting joy and happiness to The God of all ages; and were mentioned several times in the prayers to appease Him.

Even though he still felt sleepy and tired, Chief Leinad Ongoda was more than delighted to recline with his grandchildren, great grandchildren, and the entire expanse of his lineage, on the same table for the nine o'clock buffet breakfast in his mega-palatial ranch that was nestled on an undulating hill just several miles from the **Citnalta Ocean,** in the most-famous **Democratic Republic of Assusa** commonly known as **D.R. ASSUSA,** in the great continent of **Anyodha.**

The continent of Anyodha was several thousands of miles from the continent of **Ayacho** which was chief's birthplace.

The Chief really enjoyed a buffet type meal that exaggerated a great sense of variety and plenty that every man longed for. The aromas emanating from the scrambled eggs, bacon, sausage, freshly baked and toasted bread, butter, margarine, cheese, pancakes coupled with syrup, milk, coffee, tea, cereal, juices and fruits of all kinds and colors, was more than enough to tempt even a lion that had just filled his stomach to the brim.

Chief Ongoda watched his grandchildren descend on the food with tiny but firm hands and their mouths opening at irregular but natural intervals that entertained any man blessed to see his grandchildren, and eat with them on the same table.

The children knew very well not to talk with food in their mouth and observed all good table manners especially around him. Chief Ongoda had earned a reputation as a strong disciplinarian and did not take kindly to any deviant social behavior.

These were very golden or signature moments in Chief's life and he wondered why almost every summer, some of his sons and daughters would drop their children over at his ranch for several weeks at a time as they went on their vacation in the neighboring islands as was the norm of this culture.

Chief Ongoda thought that spending more time with one's children especially at their tender age or formative years, would bring much joy, elicit more pleasure and etch long-lasting signature memories for everyone in the family; But, this thought was not shared by all the civilization that lived in the continent of Anyodha as its inhabitants.

Chief Ongoda always sensed when his grandchildren wanted to ask him for a favor and this ranged anywhere from telling stories, picnicking, life-guarding them when they swam in his palatical swimming pools, or doing security when they played hide and seek, to pitching tents in the woods while camping and many other escapades or moments of thrill.

Today, he could sense that they were about to ask him for something but he did not know what it was besides, he wanted to go back to sleep after breakfast. The previous day had been a long one for him especially in the evening when he received and entertained guests in his home. Chief enjoyed parties and hosted quite a bunch of them at different times of the year.

Over the years, influential or prominent politicians, very powerful leaders in a variety of fields, industrial chiefs, presidents, intellectual luminaries, diplomats, successful businessmen, and other close confidants from far and wide, had paid him regular visits to seek his advice or counsel on a plethora of issues and to party too!

Last night after a very warm and sassy dinner, a lot of wine was served and appreciated as they wiled the night and ushered in the wee hours of the morning in their own traditional style and enigmatic fashion.

It was almost three in the morning when chief finally made it to bed and did not plan on waking up till afternoon. He was nursing a throbbing headache this morning and couldn't wait to get back to bed, but as fate would have it, that was not going to be the case today.

Chapter 2

The eating room that also served as one of the dinning rooms in the mega-palatial residence or retreat, was filled with a bunch of children, and over the time, Chief Leinad Ongoda had gave up on counting them because almost every summer, he saw some new faces amongst his descendants, and he was just as happy to know that he was blessed with many of them whatever they amounted to at any given time or in any setting worth noting.

However he always estimated their number at any given sitting and this time it was about fifty. Keeping all their names in his memory was also another Herculean task not because he couldn't do it, but because he was so busy with many other important things and opportunity cost dictated the terms of his decisions. However, Chief Ongoda knew that if he ever needed their names for any reason, he would always get them with great accuracy at any time.

Even though this seemed like a smart decision, it still bothered him what any of his grandchildren would feel or make of him just in case he couldn't remember their names.

As he pondered on this issue, he rested on the fact that a beautiful and magnificent attire that caught anyone's eye, was remembered mostly because of the major features and embroidery that it possessed however fine the fabric was. This was also true about any house or landscape or anything that Mother Nature availed unto us.

Among his grandchildren, there were many that were more conspicuous than others and displayed unique characters and upon noticing them, Chief had nicknamed them based on their character, and these ones he kept in his memory and he easily identified them whenever his eyes landed on them.

These were some of the major features and "embroidery" that caught one's eye as they appreciated the beauty and magnificence of the whole "attire" that represented his family.

However, all his children were equally important to him and he was always ready to do anything in his power to protect them whenever the need arose; and this is a truth that all of them knew and could bear testimony of.

Rieko was the first one to speak as usual. "Grandpa! Your stories are always very educative, exhilarating, inspiring yet so entertaining and captivating that we are always left hungering and thirsting for more. We know that tomorrow is the big day, but we just can't wait. Please narrate unto us the new *sigana* today, now, please..." begged Rieko.

Chief looked at Rieko with very studious eyes. Rieko had always baffled him. He was too smart for his age. His vocabulary was well above his peers. His eloquence and charisma was unique and very attractive, yet he was so humble and rational in his decision-making. His leadership over all the grandchildren was very natural and unquestionable. They was no doubt at all that they all loved him and confided in him a great deal.

Chief came to like him even the more when he witnessed a scuffle that ensued between two of his grandchildren a few summers ago.

That day, as he sat on his private patio just off his master bedroom, gazing at the sun that was just setting in the horizon over the serene and magnificent flora that encompassed his view, he heard two little voices yelling sharply.

It became very apparent that there was a misunderstanding between two young ones. "It is my turn to fly the helicopter now! It fell down when you were flying it! We agreed that if it fell down or when the battery charge ran out, whichever comes first, then you will have to give the other person the next chance to fly it! Give it to me now! Come on! Hand me the remote control!" yelled one to the other.

"No, no, no, no, no! It didn't fall down! It just rested on the leaves of this shrub! It did not fall down to the ground! It is still my turn and you have to wait for yours to come!" yelled back the other.

"This is unfair and you know it! Gimme the remote! Come on! Now!" yelled back and this time the pitch of the voice was scarier. Tempers were flaring at a dangerous rate. Chief knew that he could not ignore this scenario or scuffle at all as it could get uglier or even violent.

He craned his head above the rails to glimpse at the two and was careful enough not to be noticed. He wanted to gather as many facts as he could about this fiasco before he acted on it.

The taller one had the remote control of the toy helicopter in his hands lifted up far away from the shorter one, who was trying earnestly to reach it but to no avail. Even jumping could not help. Both faces were seriously contorted and none could hide the animosity between them. It had reached its peak.

After some frustration and constant yelling, the shorter one stepped back, took a calculated stance, fisted his arms and darted them towards his adversary's chest. The fist collided sharply with the chest and in almost the wink of an eye, both were on the ground and the chest owner was gasping for air and frantically shouting for help.

The fist owner had overpowered him and was showering him with a torrent of blows and slaps. Chief was just about to stand up when he heard another young one shouting from afar.

Chapter 3

"Hey!" The new voice exclaimed as he hurriedly continued, "Stop it! Stop it now! Tim! Josh! Stop it now or I'll….," Josh jumped off from Tim and both were sweating and trying hard to catch their breath.

While facing their arbitrator and sensing that there was some explanation needed here quickly or almost immediately or else face dire consequences, Josh was the first to speak. "It was my turn to fly the helicopter but he refused to give it to me." Claimed Josh as he pointed towards Tim.

"The helicopter did not fall on the ground! It just rested on the shrubs! It is still my turn to fly it and Josh does not wanna wait for his turn!" Tim quickly defended himself in the tone of a strong rebuttal.

The arbitrator quickly calmed them down and felt their pulses, looked at their eyes, touched the collided arrears of their bodies with the skill of a first-aid giver or a paramedic and after a few moments ordered them to sit down.

After some intelligent questioning, he found out the facts to this conflict or issue as much and as he could within the constraint of the time that he had to render a fair judgement here on this matter.

He asked one of his sisters who had also witnessed part of this fight and was now nearby, to get fetch them or bring unto them some soft drinks quickly as a supply of the much-needed energy that they had lost and the need to not only replenish the energy but also, to rehydrate themselves in the sweltering heat of this summer.

Chief Leinad Ongoda just realized that below him, under a canopy that faced this scene, were a bunch of other grandchildren who had quickly gathered or congregated to watch this scene unfold live before their eyes.

As they gulped the soft drinks, Chief Ongoda could see that the arbitrator was in a pensive mood and his eyes freely gazed into the skies as if he was trying to unravel a mystery whose solution lay in the direction of his gaze.

Definitely, he was trying to find a pragmatic solution to this squabble.

Being a very powerful and influential personality in his lifetime, Chief Leinad Ongoda had come across such situations in a myriad of ways and had an immediate and long-lasting solution for it.

However, this was a golden opportunity for him to see how his grandson was going to calm the "sea" that had otherwise just gotten rough in an instant, and try to send cool waves running down once again to the troubled hearts of the immediate parties involves, as well as all the anxious onlookers as well.

"Tim and Josh, none of you really defined what the ground really meant in your agreement." Rieko started in his judgement speech.

He continued, "This means that, both of you could have different opinions because the ground could mean different things for each one of you. So, I can either take the helicopter back to grandpa now, and you shall never see it again; or else, we can agree on the meaning of ground now, and then toss a coin and whoever wins, will fly the helicopter next. What is your decision?" asked the arbitrator.

After pondering for a while Tim and Josh agreed to toss the coin. They both liked flying the chopper and who knows what grandpa would do if he learnt what had happened. Maybe no more state-of-the-art toys anymore? They couldn't live with that and they both voiced their opinion.

Rieko proceeded by saying, "Josh! At your age, you should realize by now that there are better ways to settle disputes than using your fist! What if you fractured Tim's bones or killed him? Do you think you could have a life then? Do you stand to loose more or gain? There is a working and trusted channel of authority you could have followed.. and you know it?"

He wanted to get this over with as it was getting dark and he quickly said these words with an unquestionable finality in his voice, "We love you all! Look at your cousin! Do u really wanna hurt him?" asked the arbitrator with expectant eyes.

Josh was filled with remorse and guilt for jumping on his cousin with such anger and violence. He knew that had he not been driven by anger and taken a moment to analyze the whole situation, he would not be laddened with this heavy cross of guilt and embarrassment.

With increased seriousness in his tone, Rieko continued, "Tim! You are old enough to understand the nature of this agreement, and smart enough to find the best solution forward! You should be ashamed of yourself to have behaved this way! Is this the kind of example that you wanna set for your cousin?" Ha?" the arbitrator asked again with much more expectant eyes.

Tim was embarrassed and guilty for being selfish and taking advantage of his height and age to frustrate Josh. Almost immediately, Tim and Josh faced each other and their eyes locked but this time without any contortion or animosity.

"Now, shake hands, apologize to one another and we shall toss the coin. Come on!" suggested the arbitrator and it was at this point that Chief Ongoda nicknamed him "*Rieko*". Rieko meant "Wisdom" in Chief's native **Luo** language.

Chief Leinad Ongoda hailed from the Luo tribe that was known and recorded in the history of the land, to have settled along the shores of Lake Sango a hundreds of years ago in the continent of Ayacho, and after a long or protracted period of migration along a famous river that had its foundation or roots, affixed to this Lake.

It had always surprised Chief Ongoda as to how the Luo language blended so easily with English which was the native language here in the continent of Anyodha.

In fact, the Luo people frequently and effortlessly mixed English words with Luo words when they spoke and it normally fitted perfectly in a very conspicuous and melodramatic manner.

Perharps this is what heightened the curiosity of his grandchildren to learn more not only about the Luo language, but also the "*Luo kitgi gi timbegi*" (Luo culture and traditions).

It didn't surprise him that much that all over sudden, his grandchildren were picking up and retaining some words and phrases that they heard their grandpa speak.

For example, "*Sigana*" meant a story in the Luo language, and Rieko just used it without any struggle and everybody understood his lingo so to speak. Could it be that despite being recorded differently in the known history of origins and migration as of that day and time, maybe the Luo people and the Englishmen shared more in common than was known in present-day history!

Chief Leinad Ongoda knew that Rieko would make a very fine leader because diplomacy was naturally his way even though he had the capacity to employ violence.

The boys shook hands and one could readily tell that their eyes were watering with tears as they hugged each other reassuringly almost immediately. They were close relatives and best of friends.

While still hugging each another, they sincerely apologized to one another for having let the concepts of pride and ego, selfishness and anger come in their way. They both understood that blood was thicker than water and gave each other an assurance that they will never follow the route of violence again, in the solving of conflicts among them henceforth or moving forward.

The crowd that had gathered at the canopy clapped as they started dispersing. The coin dictated that Josh gets the next turn in the flight and being more of an expert, he taught Tim how to prevent a crash on the shrubs or any other vegetation in the vicinity. It was evident that their friendship had been cemented even more.

Chief Leinad Ongoda was impressed with the outcome of the solution and much more impressed with Rieko. He did not stand up on the balcony because he had no reason to attract their attention.

He thought about calling Rieko and praising him for a job well done, but as he sipped his rich-red wine and thought about it, he remembered an old ancestral teaching that warned about praising the palmwine tapper or the alcohol brewer as they were commonly known.

If one praised the palmwine tapper or the alcohol brewer, then he would steadily develop a tendency of diluting the palmwine with water, and the "kick" would be very hard to get or find unless one parted with more money or other forms of resources to barter or exchange for that wine or the brewed drink in question.

Rieko still had "milk behind his ears" so to speak, and being in his youth, this was time for him "to serve the best wine possible." Chief held his praises for a later day.

Of particular importance however, was worth noting that in this just-concluded or just-settled violent fiasco, the taller boy thought that his height would give him an unfair advantage over the shorter one and so he proceeded to cheat his way to afford himself a chance of flying the toy helicopter even though it was not his chance to do so and had to yield to the demands of the rules of their game.

However, to his utter dismay, the shorter boy overpowered him and managed to get his right back even though it took him time and undue effort.

Chief Leinad Ongoda knew that the other very powerfl lesson that all of them should have learnt today is that, one should never judge a book by its cover.

Now at this point, while still on the breakfast table, Chief Leinad Ongoda could tell from Rieko's face that he had been anxiously waiting for an answer from him and he expected nothing less than a yes.

Chief Ongoda looked around the room and he could see all the others hurrying with their meals in preparation for a story-telling session.

They had taken his short silence to mean a "yes". Having gained the reputation of a disciplinarian and a teacher of virtues, he knew very well that his actions must be consistent with his teachings lest he be accused of preaching water and drinking wine. Patience was the virtue at test here.

Chief Leinad Ongoda had the new story already, but what example would he be sending to his grandchildren if he granted their request today and ignored the virtue of patience which he had spent a great deal of time instilling? On the other hand, he did not feel comfortable ignoring their request.

He had to stick to his teachings regardless because this was the best time to instill these values in someone. After a certain age, it would be really hard if not impossible to shape one's value system.

Chief Ongoda always wanted his descendants to exemplify the very best of character wherever they were and it had to start with him. How was he going to satisfy these conflicting demands?

Chapter 4

"My grandchildren," Chief started while clearing his throat, "I have always narrated unto you very sensational tales from our ancestors and fore-fathers. There's no doubt at all that you have always enjoyed them and yearn for more every season. I have hopes that you always remember the relevant teachings in them, and find them useful in your day-to-day lives.

Before I narrate to you the new *sigana*, I'd like to know what you remember from the previous ones. Who can give me a summary and the teachings of any "*sigana*" (story) I've ever narrated here?" asked Chief Leinad Ongoda while he looked at the heavily expectant crowd in front of him.

Hands started laring or shooting in the air and Chief Ongoda was pleased with this response. Several hands were up now and waiting to be chosen.

This reminded Chief Ongoda of a very long time ago when he was about four or five years old. His dad almost always took afternoon siestas especially after lunch. Every time he got ready to get one, he would call Chief or any of his brothers to narrate unto him a *sigana* while he ascended in his sleep.

Chief Leinad Ongoda was chosen most of the time over his brothers. In as much as he was his father's favorite on this errand, this situation angered him because there are many times or occassions that he missed out playing with his friends outside the house while being caught up telling bedtime stories to a dad who seemed insensitive to his child's demands.

It was true however, that Chief Leinad Ongoda enjoyed telling stories or narrating them as well as reading them even though the timing of the day was not conducive, and his dad did not seem to get it even when he pretended to be sick or tired or faked some excuse.

But what was happening today was the opposite. The young ones were dying for an opportunity to narrate a tale to their grandpa who they loved very much and respected a lot. Almost all the plates on the table were empty and some children were struggling to finish their drinks in preparation for this story-telling session.

Chief thought that this spectacle or the unfolding of these events, would be very entertaining to him and was very much anxious to see how they did, especially because this was their first time.

Rieko's hand was also up, and it was then that Chief Leinad Ongoda granted him the first opportunity to tell or narrate in summary form, a "*sigana*" (story) that he remembered or was excited to narrate.

"*Chon gi lala...*" (A long time ago...), began Rieko after positioning himself before the crowd. "Along the shores of Lake Sango, there lived a man called *Nyamgondho son of Ombare*. Nyamgondho was a fisherman who plied the lake with his old canoe and fishing nets during the day, and laid *mgondho* (fish traps) during the night as was the norm or tradition of fishermen of that day to erk or make a living from the lake.

Every day, he would wake up at the crack of dawn to inspect his mgondho or fish traps. He was always anxious to see his catch because for quite a number of several seasons, luck had not been on his side even when all other fishermen boasted of their large catches and great bounties from the very same lake that he fished from.

Nyamgondho was a very bitter man and angry at life itself. He always wondered why he was even born and what purpose he was serving in this world. How come that he toiled so hard and sweated profusely yet he had nothing to show for it?

Everyday, he spent his time in the lake casting nets here and there but no fish made it to his traps. He patiently endured the scorching sun from dawn to dusk but his efforts yielded nothing. Even his fish traps barely caught anything wherever he positioned them in the lake.

Occasionally, he would find a few *"fulu"* (fingerlings) in his trap every other morning or so. His fellow fishermen always laughed and mocked at him as he watched them empty their heavy nets into several *"atonga"* (fish baskets). He had the skills and put in the efforts but he barely got enough even to feed himself.

Every evening as he treaded back to his hut bare feet, he couldn't ignore the humiliation and shame that he had endured over the years. His peers did well, had plenty and were happy with their lives even though they worked less than he did.

He looked at his tattered clothing and even though he desired new ones, he had no means to fetch them. He had nothing of value to batter for new clothing or any other thing. What a pity he was.

As he drew closer to his village. He always thought about his grass-thatched hut. Three seasons had passed without him re-thatching his roof. Everyone did their roofs before the rainy seasons so as to avoid leaks but in as much as Nyamgondho wanted to do so, he had no "*puodho*" (farm) to get roofing grass from or nothing to batter for fresh ones.

His neighbors had moved further away from him and he could dare not ask them for some much-needed roofing grass. They always whispered in low tones and laughed at him when he passed by. This evening, he knew that he was in more trouble than he had anticipated.

Nyamgondho always walked with his head facing downwards. But the instant lightning followed by the ear-crackling thunder, had suddenly illuminated the otherwise dark evening, and as he looked up in the sky, he couldn't help noticing the dark clouds that had assembled directly over the village.

The sun had retired for the day and only tired traces of its rays were visible behind the gathering of clouds. The clouds' eyes were so pregnant with rain that they started weeping as soon as Nyamgondho locked faces with them. It was no time for self pity but to run as fast as his feet could carry him.

Even though the roof of his hut was leaking, he knew that his leaking hut would provide a much better shelter than the open sky.

Despite his fatigue, he made it home just before the rain started pouring heavily. He quickly moved his *"pien"* (sleeping hides) to the part of the hut or house that didn't leak. He also removed the cooking pot that held his supper from the three-stone *"kendo"* (fireplace0 and laid it close to his *"pien"* (sleeping hides) away from the intruding *"koth"* (rain drops) that had invaded his only sanctuary.

He sat watching the rain pour down and see lightning flashing through his *"gama"* (space between the wall and the roof) and the open spaces in his roof. He endured the regular and deafening *"polo mariadore"* (thunder) even though he was scared of them. So tired he was but sleep was out of question.

Even though there was a wide space between the door and the floor that the intruding waters gushed out of the house from, Nyamgondho did not chance falling asleep lest he die in a flood.

It was common for the lake to flood and move its banks inwards towards the land and when this scenario reared its "ugly head", the villagers were often forced to move away towards the highlands or grounds of higher altitude in the terrain, until the waters receded.

Nyamgondho had hopped for a hot meal today even though he only had a few "*fulu*" (fingerlings) which he had stewed the previous night. He craved for some hot "*kuon*" (maize meal) to go with it but the rain was not relenting at all and the "*kendo*" (fireplace) was right under the gap on the roof. No fire was possible in his hut tonight.

Driven by pang's of hunger, he slowly but grudgingly descended on his cold stew of "*fulu*" (fingerlings). It tasted really good even though it was cold and barely enough to satisfy his hunger.

Nyamgondho had felt very lonely many times especially on his way home in the evenings. He could see his fellow villagers being attended to by their wives and playing with their children. Their wives cooked for them and gave them mutual comfort after a long day of toil while he returned home to himself and himself alone. No one wanted to talk to him or even associate with him.

When they so him coming on one side of the road, they went to the other. He was too poor to convince any woman to live with him. This night he really needed a companion and a shoulder to lean on but luck was very tough on him.

Tears welled in his eyes and all the pain and suffering he had endured flashed in his memory. He cried like a baby. Life had dealt him huge blows with no one in sight to comfort him or help him to deal with the immense pain that he felt in his heart.

With the rain, came a lot of cold and Nyamgondho wrapped himself with his sleeping "*pien*" (hides). He used a specially carved stone for a pillow. He had carved that himself a long time ago when he was a boy. It seemed like the rain was slowing down though not fast enough for him to go to sleep.

But he was so tired and as he thought about waking up at the crack of dawn, he decided to chance and go to sleep. The strength of his eyes were waning and it was apparent that he couldn't stay up any longer, and it was already too late. Sleep was his only medication. It was the only time he stopped thinking and could relax despite all the problems he had.

Nyamgondho thought that he was dreaming when he heard the first crowing of his neighbor's cock. He had just laid his head to rest a while ago and it was already morning! Was nature conspiring against him or what? The second crowing pierced the air and he knew that it was time to get up and head for the lake.

He made most of his catch from his fish traps than the nets. He was half asleep when he opened the door for the journey to the lake. His feet felt heavy and there was mud all over as it had rained "cats and dogs" all through the night into the wee hours of the morning. His bare feet sunk in the mud and struggled to find firm ground to walk on. It was going to be a hard walk but his determination did not waver a bit.

Several streams had snaked their way to the lake and were emptying the rain waters from the lands at varying speeds and with different strengths.

As Nyamgondho looked towards his fish traps, he could sense that something was amiss. The waters over his "*mgondho*" (fish trap)were terribly troubled. Could it be that he got a huge catch today? Could it be a big *"ngege"* (tilapia) that had strayed into the shallow waters?

Chapter 5

N yamgondho was suddenly so excited and as the thought of a big catch raced in his mind, he felt his feet getting lighter and lighter towards his fish traps. His strides widened and even though he felt like running faster towards his catch, he could not do so with relative ease due to the heavy and slippery mud on the ground that made skidding dangerously hazardous.

"Nyamgondho! Nyamgondho! Please get me out of this trap! I've been here all night! Please! Please!" a female voice yelled from the trap as he almost got there.

Chills of fear ran down his spine. His face became hot, his heart thumped like never before, his stomach tightened and he felt like diarrhea. Never had anyone had such an experience before, and neither was this a dream or a vision of some sort or kind!

As he was just about to run away, the female voice pleaded with him. Even though he tried to ignore the whole scenario and pretend that it was a bad dream, he could not do so. He looked back and it was an old lady, begging with her hands open towards him. This was a terrifying experience but the compassion in his heart at that time, jostled him to obey the voice and relieve the old woman from her seemingly undue distress.

Nyamgondho mustered the courage to approach the old lady and freed her from the traps. She introduced herself as *Nyar Nam* (Daughter of the Lake) and asked him to take her to his home for it was cold and windy. It was a bad omen to be hostile especially to older people and therefore he had no choice but to be as hospitable as he could.

She was weak and frail but could walk with ease. She leaned on Nyamgondho's shoulder as they treaded back to his home. He thought about his poverty and was embarrassed that he had nothing to offer his visitor-to-be. He was also afraid that she may laugh at him once she set her eyes on his dilapidated hut and his close-to-nothing belongings that outwardly displayed his frugal lifestlye.

But what could he do? It was the best he had and if she did not like it then she might as well go her way. Besides, Nyamgondho was just being nice to her mostly because it was a cultural demand, and deviating from such norms was known or believed to provoke *Nyakalaga's* (God's) anger or wrath on one's life and the lives of their loved ones. God had many names in this community and others referred to Him as *Obong'o,* while still others called Him *Ramogi Ajwang'*.

Nyar Nam darted to the sleeping *"pien"* (mats) immediately the door flung open. This infuriated Nyamgondho but he could not vent his anger on her since she was not only a visitor, but an old one for that matter. Which guest, especially a woman, went straight to her host's bed upon entering the house? This was unique. She made herself comfortable and covered herself except her feet since they had a lot of *"chuodho"* (mud) on them.

She looked straight at Nyamgondho and said, "I know that you have no food here, so please go and get some fish so that I can cook for you." With a lot of pain and embarrassment, Nyamgondho told her exactly what was going on in his life and how unlucky he had been. He warned her against having high expectations, since he did not even think that he would make a catch today.

Nyar Nam insisted that he go back to the lake one more time and assured him that he will make a good catch this time round. He thought that she was out of her mind and making fun of him but nevertheless he went back to the lake anyway. Besides, what other choice did he have? At least, he would satisfy his guest by trying even harder this time round.

The sun was struggling to wake up when Nyamgondho arrived at the lake again. Its rays were lazing around the sky over the light clouds and this gave Nyamgondho enough light to untie his old canoe and move it to the waters. The water was cold but felt good on his feet and he enjoyed watching the tiny ripples wash the mud off them.

He skillfully got into his canoe, checked his nets once again to ensure that he had no tears and quickly oared himself into the lake while simoultaneously easing his mind from the rigid and dictating nature of the paths that he followed to the lake, into a vastness where he was free to create his own paths or chart his own course of travel as he wished without any hindranes or obstacles whatsoever.

From the way he did it, it was clear that rowing his boat, was one of his favorite passtimes or hobby so to speak. In as much as his spirits and hopes were not that high, he nevertheless enjoyed floating on the vast lake that carried his canoe everyday. Other fishermen had started arriving and were preparing themselves to do the same.

With the nets casted in the lake, Nyamgondho focused his gaze on the horizon. He did this everyday to kill time. Fishing required a great deal of patience and no fisherman knew this better than him. He was always filled with awe and wondered how *Nyakalaga* (God) had made such breathtaking sceneries whose beauty, ambience, inspiration, awe and natural glamour, had not only captivated the attentions of all who so or spectetated at them, but also stood the test of time over and over again.

It was true tha Nyamgondho enjoyed the luscious sceneries and breathtaking horizons that laid on yonder as he marveled on the skillful hands of Nyakalaga as well as His unique wisdom in nature. Even when thoughts of his poverty began to overwhelm him, he often turned to a boat ride on the Lake and got lost in deep thought gazing at the spectacular sceneries of the lake as an integral part of his almost daily therapy.

Unlike many other times that he had gone fishing, this time round, it was interesting to note that, almost suddenly, his sightseeing was cut shot by the roughness of the waters over his net in a way that could not go unnoticed!

Nyamgondho could not believe his eyes when he saw two big *ngege* (tilapia) trapped in his net. Right before his very eyes, another one got trapped and another one! Soon he was seeing a variety of fish in his net in increasingly large amounts. Apart from *"ngege"* (tilapia), there was *"sire nyapende"* (Bagrus domac), *"mumi"* (catfish), *"okoko"* (synodontis), *"kamongo "*(African lungfish), *"ningu"* (Labeo victorianus)*"* and even *ndhira* (Abramites hypselonotus), which was famed in the community as amongst the hardest one to catch, was there in plenty!

In his excitement and experience of an almost-instant thrill, he forgot to see his canoe was now leaning dangerously on one side. The net was getting heavier and heavier and was about to tear. He quickly hurled his catch into the canoe and oared himself back to the shore as fast as he could while he struggled to stay afloat.

Even before he reached the shores of the lake, all the fishermen gazed at him in shock, disbelief and wonderment. Today he was not an eyesore anymore or a sight that one had to struggle to look at, but a sight of great respect, repute, honor and valor. With a lot of "*ich lit*" (jealousy) in their hearts, they watched him empty his net into a big "*atonga* "(fish basket). Today, they had been humbled.

Nyamgondho quickly secured his canoe and fishing gadgets in his usual spot and loaded his catch on his head. It was very heavy but he didn't mind at all. As he eased himself through the wide path into the village, he could hear from a far, several surprised exclamations from his fellow fishermen.

His height allowed him to see over the fenced homesteads that lined his path, and he could see many women staring at him and his catch with their jaws dropped and arms folded on their bosoms. Nyamgondho even heard some of them shout to their neighbors, "*Neyeuru! Bi uneye! Neyeuru Nyamgondho!*" (See! Come and see! See Nyamgondho!).

Today he was a celebrity and as he negotiated the bends along his way, the corners of his eyes caught small children and a number of villagers gazing at him from the gates of their homesteads. A true and much-needed miracle had happened to him today and he was excited, thrilled, honored and very happy indeed.

Smoke was bellowing from his hut when he got there. He wondered why Nyar Nam had started a fire without even knowing whether the *"chiemo"* (food) was going to be available to cook or not! But he was not keen on getting the answer to such questions at this moment. What mattered the most was for the food to be prepared to satisfy his hunger as well as remove the shame and embarassment of poverty and want in his house, from the eyes of his new guest even though she was still strange as such.

As he opened the door, Nyar Nam helped him to get the load off his head and carefully lay it on the ground. Beams of smiles filled her face when she saw the catch and thanked Nyamgondho for it.

Nyamgondho could see a pot full of *"dek"* (Edible weeds) on top of the *"kendo"* (cooking fire). In his absence, Nyar Nam had wondered into the nearby woods and picked the edible weeds and prepared them in readiness for the meal.

He watched Nyar Nam wash and prepare the fish for cooking and as she lowered them one by one into the *"agulu"* (pot), his appetite became more veracious than ever. He wished the fish were ready to eat but he kept his cool and as the thought for waiting for the fish to simmer engulfed his head, he stretched himself on his *"pien"* (sleeping hides) and dozed off. He was extremely exhausted and very tired.

"Nyamgondho *"chiewi!"* (Wake up!). The *"chiemo"* (food) is ready!" Nyar Nam politely woke him up. The sweet aromas emanating from the food filled his nostrils and the meal in front of him was fit for a *"ruoth"* (King).

Nyamgondho thought that his eyes were playing tricks on him and as he washed his hands, the sight of the food wetted his appetite even more. Nyar Nam had prepared a hot and mouthwatering meal of *"kuon"* (millet bread), *"rech"* (fish) and *"dek"* (edible weeds) and upon giving thanks to their God for their much-needed meal, they quickly descended on it with much relish and thanksgiving.

He knew that all food tasted good to a hungry man but he could tell that this specific meal tasted better whether he was hungry or not. Nyar Nam must have been a gifted *"jatedo"* (cook).

Nyamgondho ate until he couldn't eat no more. His stomach was full to the brim but there was still plenty waiting to be eaten! This has never happened in his life for a very long time! As he leaned the top part of his body on the wall, he noticed Nyar Nam gazing at him with a smile, and as their faces locked for a good moment, she asked Nyamgondho to take her for a wife.

No woman in his life had ever been as good to him or even wanted to talk to him. They had always rejected him and mocked him. They called him names and coined phrases that pointed to his poor and wretched life. But today Nyar Nam not only brought him luck, but also offered herself for marriage! Today, she found someone who loved him for who he was and not for whatever he had or did not have!

So much was happening to him in one day and he was careful not to make rash decisions. However he knew that this was an opportunity of a lifetime and if he failed to seize it, then it might not come again.

He stared into Nyar Nam's expectant eyes and took a good glance at her body. She was more advanced in age than he but her heart was as young, loving and tender than any he ever knew. He knew that she would provide him with everything he needed from a woman and she had proved it even without him asking for it.

Nyamgondho fell in love with her and he gladly accepted her proposal. They held each others hands and that night they shared the only *"pien"* (sleeping hides) together.

Chapter 6

*J*t so happened that Nyamgondho and Nyar Nam got along very well. Every morning at the crack of dawn, he would get up as usual and head towards the lake. This time round, his fish traps were always full and the lake teemed with all manner of fish for him. His nets were always full with a covetous variety almost as soon as he oared himself in the lake.

His jaws always dropped with wide exclamations and he wondered why he had never gotten such a catch before. He could see his fellow fishermen roll their jealous eyes at him as he struggled to get back to shore as fast as he could lest he sink due to the weight of the nets. He had rose from the losers' corner and seized the champion's position overnight in front of their very own eyes.

As he carried his catch home, he always so many villagers trying to inch towards him and wave at him; And, even the little ones had also learnt and knew his name, and shouted it in unison whenever he passed by them as they marveled at his bounty or catch. He was thrilled at this sudden change in recognition and manner of treatment.

For a long time, the same people had mocked him, whispered in low tones and burst out with laughter when they so him, and they even went as far as chanting the belittling words of *"Janeko!, Janeko!"* (Madman! Madman!). They even moved to the other side of the road when he approached from one side.

One day, he saw a woman walking out of her homestead or compound, and as soon as she saw him, she contorted her face, spat on the ground and made a u-turn back to her hut yelling very unpleasant words. The same woman nowadays greeted him and waved every time he passed by! Life had changed dramatically for him and he couldn't explain it.

Nyar Nam always welcomed him back with beams of smiles and thanked him for his hard work. It was obvious that they had more than enough to feed themselves with, and Nyar Nam processed the fish in a very skillfull manner or way. Soon the neighbors started knocking at their door and offered to batter some of their goods for some of the mouthwatering bounty that Nyamgondho brought with him every day.

45

They gladly accepted many of their battering offers. Amongst the many helter skelters of trading in his *"dala"* (homestead), Nyamgondho frequently heard several women say, *"Kata mana chuora masungorega ni en ja ywa rech moloyo ji te, pok omako machal kamae!"* ("Even my husband, who boasts to be the best fisherman of all, has never made a catch like this before!").

Within days, Nyamgondho had enough resources to build Nyar Nam a comfortable hut, fence his *"dala"* (homestead) and build several *"dero"* (granary) to store the large amounts of grains that they've been receiving in exchange for their fish. Some *"jogweng'"* (villagers) even offered large tracts of *"puothe"* (farmland) for a constant supply of fish, and this is mainly how Nyamgondho got enough land to grow all manner of grains, fruits and vegetables that thrived in those days.

Apart from being an excellent wife, Nyar Nam was very skilled in *"pur"* (farming) and *"pith"* (rearing of domestic animals). Within a couple of seasons since they started living together as husband and wife, they had managed to acquire large tracts of fertile land within their *"gweng'"* (neighborhood or village). It was Nyar Nam who worked mostly on the farm as her husband focused on his fishing career.

Being an early riser like her husband, Nyar Nam would wake up at the crack of dawn and head to her farm after ensuring that her husband had enough breakfast to energize him for the day. She also made some for herself and carried a good portion of it to snack on during her short breaks in the farm.

Within a very short time she had managed to cultivate the the land and plant "*bel*" (millet), "*kal*" (sorghum), "*oganda*" (beans), "*ng'or*" (peas), "*rabuon*" (sweet potatoes), "*budho*" (pumpkin), "*dek*" (edible weeds), and a rich variety of other edible herbs that were a favorite side dish with the local staple foods of the region.

Even popular tropical fruits like "*rabolo*" (bananas), "*mapera*" (****), "*jamna*" (grapes), "*maembe*" (mangoes), "*chwa*", "*machungwa*" (oranges), "*ndim*" (lemons), and a host of other seasonal ones, were there in plenty; And, as Nyar Nam planted and cultivated them, she made sure that they were positioned well in her farm not only for growth and harvesting purposes, but also for the aesthetic appeal of the farm.

Very soon, Nyamgondho & Nyar Nam's farm, had started attracting much attention in the neighborhood; and from the nearby hills of the village, their farm stood tall and majestic above the rest. It was the envy of the village and the neigboring regions. It was a very beautiful garden that never ran out of a harvest even in the "*ndalo oro*" (spells of dry seasons). It was a farm of great blessings even by today's standards.

In fact, during the episodes of dry seasons or dry spells on the land, it was common for people of other villages far from the lakes and more often from the "*gode*" (highlands), to travel to neighboring regions in search of a variety of food as their granaries had run out, or were at a point of running out due to the failure of the rains on the land, or the drying up of seasonal rivers that they heavily depended on in their normal day-to-day lives.

As usual, whenever they arrived in Nyamgondho and Nyar Nam's village, it was their granaries that had the most to offer; and they too made a great profit from the "*dhok*" (cows), "*diek*" (goats), "*sheep*" (rombe), "*gwen*" (chicken) and many other items that were offered to them in return for their rich supplies of food.

Soon their name began to spread far and wide beyond the borders of their villages and Nyar Nam's *"rwako welo"* (hospitality), *"tich matek"* (hard work) and *"chiwo"* (generosity), was quite unparalleled indeed; And, it earned her a lot of *"luoro"* (respect) all over.

Even strangers from distant lands were warmly welcomed, well rested and treated with great respect whenever they visited the homestead for *"ohala"* (batter trade) or some other kind of business, or just for pleasure.

Nyangondho could not believe his eyes when he saw this kind of blessings visiting his home. All that he had hoped for and desired for in life, had come true and he was living it every day to his fill and utter satisfaction.

Indeed, his prayers had been answered and he could even afford to hire *"jotich"* (apprentices, hirelings or workers) to help him offload his fish from the lake and carry it to his homestead,; And, he even hired some to take his livestock to *"kwath"* (cattle grazing).

Every day as he came back from the lake with his large bounties of fish, he took a nap as he waited for Nyar Nam to come back from the farm. Even though he cared about her and was concerned that she would be worn out due to the farm work, she insisted on making for him his meals as she really enjoyed to cook and was very good at it.

After lunch and some rest, Nyamgondho would stroll into his farm as he not only enjoyed the spectacle of great delights in them, but he also ensured that all was in order before the sun had retired for the day and disappeared behind the clouds and the endless lines of the otherwise signature and aesthetically delicate horizon.

He enjoyed walking in the shed of the "*siala*" (Nile tulip or Nile trumpet) trees that lined his path as he went back and forth to his spectacular and now one-of-a-kind gardens, and the cool touch under his feet from the soft "*lum*" (grass) that had carpeted large parts of the tracts in that vicinity.

The rich, healthy and invigorating virgin air from the farm, always filled his nostrils in a very dramatic way that encouraged him to walk faster to his farm as he cherished these moments in his life very much.

When he came back from the farm, Nyar Nam already had an "*aguata*" (calabash) of "*nyuk kal*" (Sorghum porridge) and "*rabuon mosinji*" (peeled sweet potatoes) set under a big "*yiend maembe*" (mango tree) in his homestead for him to snack on. The mango tree provided for him a great cool and peaceful shed, and many times he fell asleep under it until dinner time.

Now as was the culture of those days, a *"Jamwandu"* (rich man), of Nyamgondho's calibre, would not go unnoticed or at least celebrated by the locals or members of the same village. Not many seasons had passed before the locals in the area started to extend their hands of friendship to him.

Many were times when he intentionally refused to welcome their gesture due to the cruel, harsh and mean treatment that he had received from them during his poverty-stricken days in the past. He kept his relationship with them purely for *"ohala"* (business) purposes and nothing else.

However, as time went by, the hands of time worked its mysterious "healing magic" and he began to welcome them as friends one by one. And so it came to pass, that many of his fellow villagers had "mended their bridges" with him and he had forgiven them.

With time, it came to a point when his homestead was almost always full with *"welo"* (visitors), who had come to pay homage to him and marvel at his newly acquired wealth and stature. In the evenings they would prawl into his homestead and Nyar Nam would prepare for them an impressive feast before they retired to their own homes.

In a likewise fashion, Nyamgondho was also frequently invited to feasts and ceremonies by his own fellow villagers, *"ruodhi"* (chiefs) and other men of status in the society. As usual, during these *"budho"* (get-togethers) and extravagant lavish ceremonies, a generous amount of *"kong'o"* (alcohol), was always served to all that were of age to drink to their fill, unwind and celebrate.

However, it did not take a long time before a new trend develoved with Nyamgondho. More often than not, Nyamgondho would come back to his homestead before the darkness of the sky reached a fever pitch. He knew very well that he had business on the lake to do in the morning, and Nyar Nam was also waiting for him to return safely as was normal between a husband and a wife. She deeply cared about him and he knew it.

But with time, Nyamgondho's *"budho ma godhiambo"* (evening escapades), became notoriously more frequent, and he cared not to return to his homestead in a decent time, neither did he allow himself to sleep in another man's home because of his ego and pride.

It was very definite and obvious that he had picked up or acquired a habit that was bound to put his life in jeopardy.

Nyamgondho's "*mer*" (alcoholism) was getting way out of hand and his "*wich teko*" (tough-headedness) did not help him either. He had fallen a victim to a substance that he did not understand at all yet he claimed to know. His life was bound to take a drastic turn such as has never been seen before; And, even he himself could not believe it when nature made a drastic decision on his life due to his newly-acquired "*kido kod timbe*" (behavior and character).

Even though he had a great tolerance for alcohol, he would drink himself to a frenzy and more often than not, he would fall victim to some unwanted interactions of nature on his way home in the wee hours of the night or morning.

Sometimes, as a result of taking shortcuts on the various paths that led to his homestead, he would step on a variety of *kuthe* (thorns) that camouflaged themselves carefully in the wide expanse of grass and other forms of vegetation in the vicinity, but to him, the injuries that he sustains from these pricks and cuts, felt only like a tingle until he reached in his home.

The pain might have not been as much in the night due to the anaethetic power of the alcohol that he consumed in large sums or the sedative nature of the same; But for sure, he really felt them during the day as he sat in his boat fishing.

Very often he vowed never to go back to his drinking sprees, but when the sun almost retired back to its origin, and its rays began to lazy around the seemingly dark clouds infront of them, the urge to go back to drink, party and make merry, often overpowered him.

One night, as he left his friends homestead in a likewise fashion, he refused to heed his friends advise to stay over and spend the night due to the rains that were just about to fall. The "*nyidho*" (light rain) was a telltale sign of some impending heavy rain but Nyamgondho ignored the advise and off he went sauntering down the lane and stagerring in his normal fashion.

No sooner had he passed through a few homesteads that the rain started to accelerate very steadily and before soon he had to deal with the "*oula*" (flooding) and "*chwodho*" (mud) that was forming under his feet. He attempted to run as fast as he could but the mud under his feet did not do him any favor at all and it was just a moment later that he skid and fell like a log of tree being chopped off its roots.

He heard his *"ombong'"* (ankle) twist rapidly in a funny way and his left *"chong"* (knee) followed almost simoultaneously. Today, the pain was so overwhelming that it was like almost all the alcohol in his body had instantly turned into water or something else. Despite the pain, he mustered the courage to stand up and limp to his homestead as the rains continued to deal him a series of blows.

As soon as Nyar-Nam saw him at the doorstep of their hut, it was definite that she was shaken and was frightened to see her only husband agonizing with pain. Being the strong woman that she was, she quickly boiled some water on the *"kendo"* (stove) and used it to massage his wounds.

That night, they did not eat neither did they talk as usual before bed as it was definite that there was some explanation to be made and a new strategy or set of strategies to be adopted in order to heal their relationship before it slipped out of their hand. Serious questions had to be raised and answered in a timely manner as Nyamgondho was quickly turning into a different person that Nyar-Nam had not yet seen before.

Chapter 7

*Ꭲ*yamgondho could not make it to the lake that morning due to his injuries and so he decided to stay at home. Nyar-Nam also decided to take a day off from her farming routine to nurse her husband's wounds. She only sent a "*jatich*" (worker/laborer) to tend the daily chores of the farm as she was a greatly dedicated "*japur*" (farmer) and very had-working worman with a strong work ethic even in times when the villagers got lazy to tend to their farms or work on their normal household chores.

Funnily enough, husband and wife did not talk to each other that much during the day unless it was just neccessary for politeness purposes or to satisfy the demands of mutual respect that out to be in a relationship of that manner, sort or setting.

There was more silence in their homestead that day than has never been there before and the "*jotich*" (workers / laborers), could notice it. Even without being told, they knew that their masters were going through a rough time, and the normal *"kwoth"* (gossips), began going back and forth within the homestead.

That evening after dinner, Nyamgondho decided to lay on the sleeping hides that was their bedding too. It was usual for Nyar-Nam to sit by the *"kendo"* (fireplace) while sipping on some cold water from the large *"aguata"* (calabash) as it not only helped with the digestion of the food in her stomach, but it also helped to cool down her body and whatever remained of it, she could use to kill the fire or put it out as they retired to the bed for the night.

After taking a few gulps of *"pi"* (water) and simoultaneously pondering on the issues of the day, she could not help to notice the shadows on the wall being cast by the illuminating power of the flames from the steady fire that leaped from one side to another in the fireplace as if they were dancing a rythmic song or sending a coded or encrypted message to those who were able to decode it.

It was actually the shadow of Nyamgondo as he lifted his front part of the body and sat on the sleeping mat while resting on his hands. Quickly, Nyar-Nam took a glance at her husband to inquire if he was in need of any help but his eyes sent a signal that he was fine and was just recapurating from his injuries. He confirmed this almost simoultaneously with a nod.

It was Nyar Nam who broke the silence between them that evening when she finally decided to confront him with the tough questions that had troubled her mind for long. With great courage but unique politeness and humility, she quietly asked Nyamgondho, "My husband, "*osiepna*" (my friend), what is it that has happened between us that you have nowadays decided to make other places more of your home than your own "*dala*" (homestead)?

You hardly ever eat dinner at home? Even the "*welo*" (visitors) that often come by, cannot "*neni*" (see you)? We hardly ever find time to "*nyiero*" (laugh), talk freely or even spend time together as we used to do? Why are you abandonding your "*dala*" (home) for the love of "*osiepe*" (friends)? Why so much "*mer*" (binge drinking) at "*gotieno*" (night)? Don't you also have "*kong'o*" (alcohol) in your homestead that you can also drink freely?

Before Nyar-Nam could go any further with her inquisitive questioning, Nyamgondho sharply interjected in a very rude and shocking manner and almost barking as a dog. With seething anger, he began to yell, "*Dhakoni!* (This woman)!, "*Bende ing'eyo ni iloso gi dichuo?*" (Don't you realize or know that you are talking with a man?) In whose "*dala*" (home) are you living in? "*Kik imien koda weche*" (Don't argue or question me), or else "*Abiro milo wang'i apat nyowuoyo.*" (I will slap you thoroughly).

Nyar-Nam looked at him carefully as he uttered these threatening words and it was clear that there were daggers in his eyes. "*Adwaro mondo ichik iti mondo iwinja malong'o kabisa*" (I wan't you to listen to me clearly). "*An dichwo mang'ongo e gweng'ni*" (I am a man of great reputation now in this society), "*koro adwaro nyithindo*" (now I want children), "*kod mon mang'eny ka luore gi kaka duong'na chal kae*" (and more wives to match my reputation and status in this society).

"*Koro nyaka aser mon kendo alombgi mondo arwakgi e dala kae*" (Now I have to seduce women and entice them to be part of this homestead). "*An kaka dichwo, anyalo timo mano kaka adwaro*" (I as a man, I can do that as I wish). "*Nitiere ma oseyie bedo nyieki*" (There are those who have already accepted to be your co-wives), "*kendo wuonegi oseyie miya gi*" (and their fathers have accepted to give them to me).

"Omiyo gibiro biro e dala kae mapiyopiyo" (And they are scheduled to come to this homestead very soon), *"to nyaka irwakgi kaka mikayi!"* (And you have to welcome and accept them as your co-wives!). *"Bende iwinja malong'o dhakoni? Iwinja maber dhakoni?"* (Are you getting me well? Woman! Have I made myself clear?).

Nyar-Nam could not believe her ears when she heard her only husband communicating to her in that fashion and uttering very painful words that hit her like a rock falling off a cliff or a landslide from the top of a very steep mountain. Almost immediately, she felt really funny in her stomach and became dizzy for a while as she struggled to deal with this sudden change of events in her life.

As she tilted her head to the ground while searching for the appropriate answers to her husband's demands, she could not ignore the fact that in that time, the culture of that tribe, allowed men to marry as many wives as they could take care of if they decided to chose to do so. In fact, several men in the village and villages nearby, had multiple women as wives in their homesteads.

It was also a fact that she had not bore any children and that her husband might be yearning for children even though it was not abnormal for one not to have children in their marriage. There were several women who were not able to bear children for quite a number of reasons but they still lived a happy, peaceful and envious life in their *"mieche"* (homesteads).

Also, the tone, seriousness and urgency in Nyamgondho's voice, suggested that he was going to do it anyway, even if she thought otherwise or had an alternate opinion. Nyamgondho's greed, and haste in life, blinded him on the fact that Nyar-Nam was a woman of great *"midhiero"* (mystery).

As she juggled all these thoughts in her head, Nyar-Nam could also not avoid the fact that time was of the essense here and her response was required in a speedy fashion lest the situation get out of hand and turn violent or even worse.

What worried Nyar-Nam most, was the safety of her husband especially while he walked back home in the wee hours of the night while drunk to a stupor and staggering from one side of the road to another. She greatly feared that the marauding *"otoyo"* (hyenas) that often strayed from the nearby *"thim"* (forest) in search of their prey, would one day attack Nyamgondho and kill him very painfully. The hyena's attacks were known to be very veracious and mean-spirited indeed.

The hyenas were notorious for *"nyiero"* (laughing) like human beings from a *"metho"* (drinking spree) as they lay in wait for their prey; And, due to the fact that Nyamgondho liked to drink and hang out with drunkards, he could easily fall into the trap of the hyenas and disappear for ever!

If Nyamgondho's desires for more wives in their homestead would prevent him from taking these huge risks in life, then it would be a better option than staying out late every day. It would give her some form of peace in the mind to yield to his demands even though she did not agree with them at all.

It also shocked Nyar-Nam that her husband and her always consulted on major issues before they made strategic long-term decisions in their life; But this time, Nyamgondho had taken a great departure to their normal decision-making process, and this major deviation, was a real concern to her.

His decisions were made with great haste, quite unilateral and final without any room for questioning or any comments. Nyamgondho's pride, tough-headedness, arrogance, selfishness and ego had grown to a fever pitch.

With great pain and sorrow in her heart, she lifted her head slowly and faced Nyamgondho who was now looking at her sternly and impatient to hear from her. She bent her face to the side slightly as she uttered a few words to the effect that she did not object to his wishes while also making sure that her body language made it clear that she did not welcome the idea at all but was forced by the circumstances at hand to make a concession that would work between them and keep the relationship going.

Nyar-Nam finished by saying that, "*Awinji*" (I here you), "*Ang'eyo kendo koro aneno ka ndalo machon mane in kendi,*" (I know, and now I see that a while back when you were alone), "*to ne ok in dichuo,*" (You were not a man), "*to tindeka wasebedo kanyo achiel,*" (But nowadays, when we have become one), "*to koro in dichuo*" (You are now a man), "*kendo koro idwaro timo mana dwachi.*" (And now you just want to do whatever you want to do). "*Eeh!*" (Oh Yes!) "*Tinde wiyi tek kabisa.*" (Nowadays you are a tough-head), "*Wiyi tek ka okoko wuon pala.*" (Your head is as tough as the *Sinodontis petricola* fish).

"*Okoko*" (Sinodontis Petricola), was a common fish in the region. It often resided in the muddy or swampy parts of the lake and was known for its very tough skull, uniquely slithery-spotted skin and shortness in length. It was in the family of catfish and bore the resemblance and spotted skin like a leopard. Some called it the water leopard.

It however, made very good soups and was very tasty and nutritious especially when served with *"alot"* (a mixture of vegetables) and *"Kuon"* (kuon). The characteristic toughness if its head stood out so much that a common phrase was coined by the people of that community to describe a tough-headed person.

At that point, Nyamgondho did not really care whatever she said. He had already gotten his message across or relayed it across in order to satisy the demands of protocol in his traditional or culture, and was on his way to planning on introducing his to-be new wives to Nyar-Nam as soon as his wounds healed up.

After all, who was a woman to her, let alone a woman's voice? He said pridefully and with disrespect in his heart, *"Dhako adhaka ni! Dhako en ang'o kuoma?"* (Just a woman! Who is a woman to me?). He had the wealth to buy as many as he wanted and so long as he got his way, he didn't really care.

He quickly laid his body back on his beddings and acended into his sleep with the only worry of recoving as soon as is possible in order to seal the deals of getting his to-be wives to join him in his matrimonial home, and be sealed to him for ever.

Meanwhile, Nyar-Nam took the calabash of water that was in her hand and poured the last bit of it onto the embers in the fireplace to kill it as she prepared to lay down. She got an extra mat and unrolled it on the floor and as she laid down on it, tears rolled down on her cheeks as she remembered the pains, trials and tribilulations that had gripped many homesteads in which plural wives had been accepted as part of the family tradition.

The jelousies, seething anger, rampant quarells, and even premature deaths resulting from the internal feuds in these families, worried and saddened her beyond measure. That night, *"paro"* (thoughts), kept on visiting her mind one after the other and before long, it was dawn. It was clear that sleep had eluded her. As nature would have it, it was only a matter of time before her homestead became a theatre of serious drama that had yet to unfold in the history of mankind as was known at that time and even today.

Chapter 8

At the first crow of the cock, Nyar-Nam was already up and ready to handle the chores of the day despite the torments of the previous day and the sleepless night that she had endured so painfully due to no fault of her own. She immideately summoned the *"jotich"* (workers) and delegated responsibilities to them in a timely manner due to the fact that she had to still nurse the wounds of her husband.

The herds of cattle, sheep and goats were ready to go out in search of pastures and the *"jakwath"* (Herdsman) was present to tend to them. Other workers went on to the farm to tend to the fields while she hurried to let the *"gwen"* (chicken) out of their *"asere"* (roosting nets) to fend for their daily food around the *"dala"* (homestead). She harvested the *"tong"* (eggs) in the nests and carefully secured them in her hut for their regular food supplies.

She also sent one of the workers to inform their *"osiepe machiegni"* (close friends) on Nyamgondho's recent *"masira"* (accident) as was usual in those days. Later on she made some *"nyuka"* (porridge) and *"rabuon"* (sweet potatoes) for breakfast; And, after eating with her husband, she left to some nearby bushes in search for the relevant *"yath"* (medicinal herbs) that she would later administer to her husband to help with his much-needed quick and speedy recovery.

Nyar-Nam was also known to be naturally gifted in *"thieth"* (medicine) and during those times, traditional herbs and roots were used to help in the healing and recovery of common ailments, diseases and other complicated medical conditions. Where she got the gift, no one knows and no one questioned either, and all they knew was that her treatments worked superbly and was also the best pain reliever in times of physical pain due to maladies or all forms of ill-health that they knew of or came accross.

Her trip to the nearby bushes around the homestead and her farm, turned out to be very successful as she managed to pick up some relant weeds and dug some roots as medication for her husband. When she returned home, she quick lit up a fire in her hut and brought the water in an *"agulu"* (pot) to a boil, added the mixture of herbs and waited for a few minutes for the medication to mix thoroughly. She later used them to massage Nyamgondho's wounds while others were given to him orally.

Prescribing and administering medicine was trully a gift especially in those days and times; and there was no doubt at all that Nyar-Nam was a *"jathieth"* (herbalist) who knew *"yien"* (medicine) very well. In fact, neigbhors, close friends and other villagers came at various times of the day, to comfort him and wish him a quick recovery. Nyar-Nam was in charge of all these programs and received them very well and with *"luoro"* (respect). They also ate and drank to their fill before they left or retired to their homes.

In about a week or so, Nyamgondho recovered from his injuries very well and was back to his normal routine. Up and about, bouncing like a young man again with great vigour and virile energy dashing in his veins, he hardly even used a cane to go back and forth to his fishing duties. He drunk lots of *"kado"* (soups) of *"rech"* (fish) and *"orenge"* (hooves of cattle).

Orenge soup was a very common staple and was known and believed to help in the speedy healing of wounds both internal and external. In fact, when the men often returned back from a "*lweny*" (war or battle) with many wounds and sores, Orenge soup was one of the first foods to be made available for their consumption.

Even when the young men were done with their regular friendly "*amen*" (wrestling) matches, they all knew that some orenge soup was waiting for them in their mother's or grandmother's homes.

And so, Nyamgondho quickly recovered and in no time at all, started his project of installing co-wives into his homestead. He visited the homesteads of these families accompanying himself with gifts and a number of "*dhok*" (cattle) to present to the parents of his new-to-be wives as dowry. Several talks were held back and forth and so many days passed by as the new co-wives prepared themselves to be installed into their new homes.

It was customary in those days that each co-wife have her own "*ot*" (hut) in the same homestead as the other wives and there was an order in which they were to be built. The first hut/house, was the one at the farthest from the gate of the homestead but facing the gate. It was the "*ot maduong'*"(main house) upon which all the visitors would be welcomed, and major or important official matters of the home would be addressed. It was the headquartes of the home and in this case, it was Nyar-Nam's hut that served this purpose. It was called *od mikayi* (The firs't wive's house).

The second wive's house would be built on the right hand side of the *Mikayi's* (First wive's) house, and the third wive's house was build on the left hand side of the first wive's house but directly opposite the second wives house.

The fourth wive's house was built next to the second wive's house but towards the gate and further from the main house. The fifth wive's house was built next to the third wive's house but directly opposite the fouth wive's house. So the trend would continue that way and in that fashion as per how many wives the man wanted to install in his "*dala*" (homestead) and was ready to take care of.

What surprised Nyar-Nam even more, was the number of co-wives that were being installed within a relatively short period of time. Nyamgondho was behaving like a "*jawuoro*" (greedy person) with an insatiable quest for overindulgence in the merry-making aspects of mankind, and especially the consumption of *"kong adhing'a"* (local brew).

It greatly bothered her but she dared not to stop him lest it lead into another *"dhao"* (quarel). Her position in the homestead as the *"Mikai"* (first-wife) carried with itself a lot of responsibilities and she had to carry herself in a special manner and set a good example for the rest.

And so Nyar Nam watched every so often when new co-wives were installed one after another and grass-thatched huts built from down to top to house them. She welcomed them warmly as it was her duty to do so and made them feel at home. They in turn gave her the respect she deserved and got to know the homestead and the routine in this new environment.

Each and everyone of them was given a portion of *"puodho"* (farm land) in order to cultivate and use the harvest to run their houses. They also got a fraction of the catlle, sheep, goats and chicken to attend to and supplement their supplies.

This was a pinnacle prerequisite and requirment for a man interested in marrying. In fact, according to the culture and tradition of the times in that community, it was normal and customary for the parents-in-law of the woman to be married, to verify first, that their daughter was going to get these things first before releasing her to her would-be husband. This ensured that she was going to be economically stable and also, that she or her children, would never die of *"kech"* (hunger).

Several feasts and celebrations were held in the homestead almost every so many days and there was *"mor gi kwe"* (happiness and peace), and harmony amongst the wives. Nyamgondho even started coming home early and would spend more time in the home rather than outside as he used to do so. He had a choice of sleeping in any house he desired in his *"dala"* (compound) and he pleased himself as he wanted. However, a couple of seasons passed by before a new train of events started gripping the home.

Nyar Nam had noticed in many occasions, that all his co-wives had a rather unique appreciation for *"kongo"* (alcohol) than was rather usual. While not many women in those days drank alcohol, it was true that some women had an accentuated taste for it especially the ones that actually brewed it or were actively involved in its distribution. The women who consumed alcohol, did it responsibly but these ones were a rare breed.

They waited almost every day after Nyamgondho had exited the homestead for the lake to fish as usual, and within no time, they would get together in one of the women's hut and hit the "*oseke*" (popular slang' for alcohol) in large quantities.

It was usual in those days for alcohol to be served in one big pot and the men would sit around it on small stools; and each of them had a long hollow reed that they used as a straw for drinking. They would insert it normally into the pot and each would sip at their own leisure and pleasure. It was this long hollow reed that was called "*oseke*". People of "*oseke*" were therefore known to be alcoholics, and these women were in the same level as Nyamgondho if not worse.

Nyar Nam always went on by her business and occasionally warned them of this habit. What if they got pregnant and bore the much-desired children that Nyangondho wanted, would they raise their children while getting drunk all day and moving around in a daze? What if important visitors arrived in the homestead, would they be sobber enough to welcome them in a respectable way? What if they had a "*masira*" (accident or emergency) in the homestead, would they be in the right shape of mind to respond to it responsibly? What if their own parents came to visit them, would they still behave the same?

As she posed these thoughtful questions again and again to them in the most humble but stern way possible, she quickly realized that she was creating more *"wasigu"* (enemies) than *"osiepe"* (friends); She was creating more foes than allies.

Everytime she passed by, the mood changed amongst her co-wives and after she disappeared around the corners of the windy path headed to her farm, she would hear them giggle with laughters, sulks and disrespectful murmurs designed to insult someone.

So she ignored them for a while and focused on the daily chores of the homestead until one season, she could not bear it no more. As she walked through other parts of her farm that was allocated to each wife, she found out that the crops had not been weeded for a long time and the *"buya"* (weeds) was almost taking over the farm.

This was a huge waste of *"kodhi"* (seeds) and farm land. It was apparent that her co-wives had been consumed by their alcohol and merry-making ordeals that they forgot to tend to their farms. This greatly angered Nyar Nam as she knew that the *"dero"* (granaries) would not be as full as is neccessary to run the homestead as the harvest would be close to nill at this rate.

This was an eye-sore to the family as a whole and she decided to approach Nyamgondho with this matter; and as the head of the household, he would decide on what to do. Maybe they could hear his voice better than hers. She continued on her way as she thought of the best way to approach Nyamgondho and the right time to do it.

It is a painful truth that many homesteads, marriages, relationships or even groupings of people, often broke or disintegrated whenever there was a confilict or a set of conflicts to be solved not that much because the conflict resolution teams involved were wrong or irresponsible, but because the TIMING of these conflict resolution meetings was not taken into deep or serious consideration.

It is indeed true that things done correctly but at the wrong time, can still yield devastating results and destroy the profit as well as erode the goodwill of relationships in general; And, Nyar Nam knew this even the most. He, Nyamgondho, normally got irrate after drinking so it had to be right after dinner before he started his drinking sprees and merry-making nonesense that Nyar Nam found it wise to approach him with this matter.

That night after dinner in the "*ot mang'ongo*" (main house), Nyar Nam carefully and quickly approached him with the issue. It was true that Nyamgondho really liked his farms and could not afford the embarassment that would engulf him if the "*gweng'*" (village) if the "*jogweng*" (villagers) would come to know that his farms are not yielding as much as they should be. For once after a long time, Nyar Nam so his husband take a responsible stance and make a wise decision, and in a timely fashion or manner.

Nyamgondho, quickly called a "*jatich*" (laborer) to his presence and ordered him to summon all his wives to the main house as there was an emergency "*bura*" (meeting) that had to be held, and it had to be held now and no later.

Within a short while, they had gathered in the "*od mikayi*" (First wive's) house and sat themselves on the mats that had been prepared on the floor. It was apparent that some were already drunk while others were fixing to do the same but they feared Nyamgondho's wrath and so they did not miss the meeting.

As he sat confidently on his majestic stool, Nyamgondho opened the meeting. *"Kawuono, bura ni dwaro bedo machiek to kendo manigi lweny mager kabisa kod golo kido mar samwoyo kod yomyom ma osechako donjo e dalani kendo koro dwaro goye piny."* (Today, this meeting is going to be short, and with a lot of seriousness of removing the character of laziness and procrastination that has started to encroach in this homestead and it now wants to destroy its wealth as well as its reputation).

While in a very angry but sincerely concerned tone, he continued to say, *"Dalani en dala ma rahuma ma ok wanyal bedo ni puothewa ok pur to kendo ok do!"* (This is a homestead of great repute and msterious wealth that we cannot afford to ignore the much-needed cultivation required on our farmlands!)

He added, *"Puodho nyaka ipur, kendo ido maber mondo eka cham owuogie mang'eny kaka dwarore."* (A farm has to be well cultivated and also the crops well weeded in order for the harvest to be large enough as is wanted.)

Nyamgondho continued to make it clear that, *"Joma Nyap ok adwar kata matin e dalana kae."* (I do not want lazybomes or lazy people here in my hoestead.)

He added "*An jaduong' mang'ongo kabisa e gweng' ni to atiyo pile pile! Un utimo ang'o kae makelo dongruok?*" (I am a very respectable man in this community but I work every day! What productive thing are you people doing here?)

In a very harsh and authoritative voice, he made it clear that, "*Ndalo ka okalo ka pok ayudo ka puothe manigi buyago ok odo maber, to boka rao emanaket e laro kae ma aduoku ka wuonew gi minew kucha!*" (In a few days if I see that those farms have not yet been weeded properly, I will take my special whip that is made out of the hippopotamus skin, and use it on you, as I drive you back to your parents' home!)

With a finality in his voice, Nyamgondho concluded unto them by affirming that, "*Kendo abiro wero maber chuth, ka aseduokou e thucheu kuno.*" (And, after I have returned you back to them, I will get back or recover all the dowry that I paid to your parents when I married you.)

As the "*Wuon dala*" (Head of the household), he had the authority to conclude the meeting at anytime, and he ended the meeting my saying unto them that, "*Ageno ni uwinjo wachni malongo. Bura orumo.*" (I hope that you have heard me clearly. End of meeting.)

His facial expressions coupled with the tone of his authoritative voice made it clear that this was a one way conversation.

Even the finality of his words revealed that a lot of his seething *"ich wang'"* (anger) was stemming from how many of his *"puothe"* (farms) were carelessly being attended to. None of the co-wives dared to lift their voice as they knew that this was not a man to be joked around with.

After some noticiable tense silence, Nyamgondho said unto them, *"Ero koro agonyow e budho ni. Doguru e uteugo. Kendo ok adwar koko e dalani kendo!"* (Now, I have finally released you from this meeting. Go back to your houses. And I don't wanna hear any noise or conflicts in this homestead again!)

He continued by adding a very vivid or graphical threat unto all of them saying that, *"Arunguna mar atug diep bende an kodo kae. Ka ng'ato dende ile to mondo ogo nyoho sanie! Dhiuru kucha!"* (I also have with me my very biggest club, cudgel or bludgeon that is famed to make one diarrhoea on impact. If anyone of you is itching for some fight, I dare you to provoke me now! Get out of here!)

No sooner had Nyamgondho finished uttering these words, that he so all the guilty co-wives of Nyar Nam scampering for safety as they hurriedly left the venue of this one-of-a-kind and first-time-ever *"bura"* (meeting) in this *"dala ma rahuma"* (famous homestead).

It was clear that the *"Jaduong' dala"* (Head of household) had spoken.

As it is true that every cloud has a silver lining, one thing about Nyamgondho that stood out the most, is that he was he was hard-working man and also a person who was known in his native language as a *"Jakinda"* (A diligent person).

In fact, as history would record it later on from a sincere or honest perspective or opinion devoid of favor and full of objective observation, in the entire village that Nyamgondho lived in, no man there defeated him with this characteristic trait of *"kinda"* (diligence).

"Nyamgondho ne en jakinda kabisa kendo jatich matek to kendo mano e kaka ne osero hawi ei dalane." (Nyamgondho was a very hard working man and very diligent and this is how he attracted or seduced luck or the favor of God into his homestead.)

Whatever inspired him to work, inspired him good enough. Could it be that, he did this because it was the thing that he enjoyed to do, or he was actually hiding a deep-seated opposite characteristic trait, that would later on be evident once he had acquired the "*mwandu*" (wealth), "*huma*" (fame), and "*luoro*" (honor) and needed Nyar Nam mo more in his life?

Chapter 9

*J*t so happend that in the following or successive days, Nyar-Nam's co-wives normal *"timbe maricho"* (bad habits) and their evil and egoistic tendencies that were addressed in the previous bura (meeting), had been almost abolished if not totally abolished at least to the eyes of a not-so-keen observer.

It was a pragmatic or practical truth that Nyamgondo and all of them were changing dramatically and even the farms that had gone unattended for so long and known for wasting seeds and the labors of cultavation that had gone into them, were actually now amongst the best and even could even qualify as "choice-bread" amongst all the farmlands that belonged in that homestead.

In fact, Nyar Nam even wondered why in as much as Nyamgondho was a very hard-working and diligent man, he failed to notice the *"nyao"* (laziness), *"galruok"* (procrastination) and the pronounced *"ywaruok"* (dragging of feet in his homestead) for quite a protracted period of time as to even threaten the now-coveted status, prominence and wealth of his homestead.

However, she knew that it was the negative effects of excessive alcohol consumption and actually alcoholism that was slowly but steadily taking root in Nyamgondho's life, and in as much as he avoided to "take the bull by the horns" in the tackling or addressing this matter, it still remained his God-given choice to do so and not any other person's priviledge even if they felt otherwise.

Nyar Nam was a very God-fearing woman with stellar moral ideals even to be famed as impeccable not only in the entire village, but also in the sorrounding *"gwenge"* (villages) and places of habitat beyond the *"gode"* (hills) that were hidden by the horizons, and the impeccable sunsets of the otherwise beautiful landscape or terrain of the land that was enjoyed by these relatively humble people but with a few *"olembe maricho kae gi kacha"* (bad apples here and there).

God is very strange and so Nyar-Nam thought and often reflected not only on the strangeness of God's character and His boundless love as well as His much-needed tender mercies, but also marveled at how He allowed evil to take root on the land and used it to educate its inhabitants never to be rooted in evil, but to focus their gaze and utmost reliance on Him who was known to them in their native language by many names such as *Obong'o, Nyakalaga, Were* and even as *Ramogi Ajwang'* to some people or elders in that community who understood their ancestry in an accentuated manner as well as cherished the reverence of their God by observing His dictates and dictums of praise and worship.

Earlier on in her strange life before she met Nyamgondho, Nyar Nam had come across and internalized many teachings of God that not only guided her decision-making or train of though in the making of choices in her day-to-day life, but wise teachings that she had internalized well enough as to be part of her nature, character, way of life or culture, tradition, norms and even an integral part of her lifestyle that no one including her co-wives could deny was part of her definition and worth emulating for all human beings; And. at the crescent of it, was "*bolruok*" (humility).

How she wished that her young co-wives could spend time with her in order to learn from her the "*midhiero mag piny*" (secrets of nature) that would strengthen their personal homes in their large homestead and even secure it as well as maintain the survival and longevity of their family lineage not only in their own generations, but also in generations to come.

It was like they were not taught to pursue such endevors from the very "*mieche*" (homesteads) that they sprouted or originated from. Perhaps these women might have been a victim of bad parenting or from "*mieche maricho*" (broken families) that appeared to the observers as descent and respectable yet trully broken inside and full of skeletons in the closet that had to be dealt with before the children could be given into or presented for marriage purposes.

Although they were lazy, very egotistic, and did not comprehend that much that in as much as a lazy lifestyle was a comfortable way of life, it is indeed a guarantee and a sure path to self-destruction, poverty, want and disease; And even a precusor to painful death and destruction of both self and society.

Even though, out of her own heart, she sincerely sympathized with them and how she wished that they at least would heaken or pay attention to some "*puonjruok*" (teachings) that she had learned a long time ago from a person of great moral authority who shared with her such noble words as follows: "Take a lesson from the ants who despite the seasons of drought and spells of harsh weather conditions, they never lack food to eat and even shelter. But any time that you see ants, unless they are dead, what do you see them do?"

Also, this man of authority further shared with her, the following story, "I went by the field of the slothful, and by the vineyard of the man void of understanding; And, lo, it was all grown over with thorns, and nettles had covered the face thereof, and the stone wall thereof was broken down. Then I saw, and considered it well: I looked upon it, and received instruction. Yet a little sleep, a little slumber, a little folding of the hands to sleep: So shall thy poverty come as one that travelleth; and thy want as an armed man.

One of the pinnacle or amongst the most pronounced observations that she made from Nyamgodho's character and behavior was that, he was a man who liked very much to "*bayo*" (wondering about), and a lot of wondering about he did indeed.

She also noted that, it was mainly for this reason that along his loitering and wondering about aimlessly or "*bayo*", that she met other women who were commonly known as *"mon mabayo"* (Women who wonder about), and even of *"chode"* (loose morals) and possesed characteristic traits that are often not rooted or grounded on a solid foundation of sincerety of heart especially when it came to matters of mutual trust, honesty, integrity, fidelity especially in marriage, endurance in love, cordiality of relationships and even the massaging of relationships that are deemed to endure or weather the storms of life even in *"ndalo mag oro"* (Seasons of dry spells or drought, poverty or want) where true love and its endurance is trully tested.

There were times when *"dhao"* (quarrels and misunderstandings) almost got out of hand amongst the co-wives especially when Nyamgondho who was the head of the homestead was not around.

Some of those domestic feuds or domestic rows became loud and had it not been for the presence of Nyar Nam, the *"Mikai"* (First wife) and her affirmative authority in the homestead, these women would have even *"negre"* (killed) themselves or sustained serious *"hinyruok"* (injuries) from their back and forth alcohol-instigated fist fights and slaps inspired by *"mbaka mag oyuma"* (rumours and gossips), and unique levels of *"lauruok kod piem marach"* (jelousy and unhealthy competition) between the co-wives.

Aparrently these were women that Nyamgondho had met and befriended from various *"ute mag kong'o kod chode"* (Places known for the brewing, selling and consumption of alcohol as well as sexually provocative dancing and related activities).

It was his *"mer mokalo apima"* (binge drinking) that became more alarming to Nyar Nam and many days, weeks, months and seasons went by as she did her best to contain the damage of this behaviour in her homestead without "stepping on the toes" of his *"nyiekene"* (co-wives) and "ruffling the feathers" or ruining, or putting into jeopardy the cordial and respectful relationships that she enjoyed with her relations from these families.

She was an undoubtably a *"ng'ama ng'ongo"* (figure-head) and a symbol of authority not only in her homestead but also in the entire *"gweng"* (village). However, of particular importance was the first co-wife that ever stepped into this homestead and was accepted and installed as a co-wife through the normal and traditionally-accepted methods.

In most of the *"koko"* (domestic rows or feuds) in the homestead, her involvement featured the most even if she was not there physically as she was a person greatly known for her *"kwoth kod thuo ji"* (back-biting and inspiring conflict).

Even though she had a short-stature, she was physically strong and was a force to recon with when it came to *"amen"* (wrestling) or *"dhao"* (physical fights). Many of her co-wives, had learnt the hard way that she was not the type to be bullied or to be picked on, and some already had *"mbala"* (marks) or their bodies and different types or kinds of blemishes on their *"del"* (skins) due to being involved in these fights.

She talked a lot especially after drinking or consuming alcohol and it was in such drinking sprees that her characters of *"kuotho"* (back-biting), and *"mirima mang'eny"* (sharp temper), came to be known without any doubt even to they who were not of that homestead.

She quickly gained a repution for cooking up of *"miriambo"* (lies), and calculated deceits or deceptions geared towards tearing down the houses of her co-wives with the main aim of being the only loved wife of Nyamgodho.

In the way she carried herself, spoke and even interracted with the community, it was obvious to they who were close observers, that she only married Nyamgondho for his reputable wealth or fortune and not that much out of true love that endures to the end.

In fact, several times, it was heard amongst the conversations between the "*mon*" (women) in that village that she might have been a "*jajuok*" (witch) or a "*jasihoho*" (One who is engaged in witchcraft or occult science), who casted her black magic spell on Nyamgondho in order to marry her.

It was her "*ot*" (hut) or house that was the closest to Nyar Nam's house in the "*dala*" (homestead) and many are times when the corners of Nyar Nam's eyes would catch her staring at her strangely with evil or deceitful eyes that were hard to detect to the untrained or inexperienced person in relations of such kind.

Interestingly enough, despite knowing or sensing what was in her mind, Nyar Nam often kept her "cool" and never inquired from her the true nature of her deeply-hidden animosity towards her, or even brought the subject to the table for discusion even though it was apparent that she was very much covetious of Nyar Nam's position in the homestead as the "*Mikayi*" or First wife in the homestead and family, and unopposed even as the cultural rules and norms as well as the traditions of the people instituted, instilled, fostered, inculcated, and even sustained unquestionably.

In fact, Nyar Nam's first co-wife was not only a pathological liar, but was also one who was known to create in her mind ideas of great deceit or deception way long before they actually materialized in the physical realms of existence or even in the material world where normal people lived in and where true peace, happiness and joy were yearned for. Order and sincere truth and justice was never her way of life or choice if values as they had now known or even understood her so far in the "*dala*" (homestead).

There are several days that even her co-wives who had been officially installed in that homestead or come into that "*dala*" much later than her, had thought in their own lifes of how to actually get rid of her company in their own very houses or cocoons or when their relatives we're visiting as they feared that her cunning ways would secretly be at work in order to break or jeopardize the longevity of their marriage or living in that home altogether.

It was apparent that she was a "*jawuor*" (a greedy pig) for that matter, and did not like the success or the celebration of a bounty from another person's home or the enjoyment of the fruits of the labors of their hands, brow or sweat.

In as much as they knew and intensely experienced these feelings, many of them were afraid to say or voice their opinions in person for fear of her "*goch*" (fist-fighting) or her "*amen*" (wrestling) matches especially when she was drunk and in the true middle of her celebration of her behavior and her character as it was known.

Interestingly enough whenever new visitors came to the home, her demeanor completely changed, and in fact, it was hard to convince the visitors that she was actually of the character that was opposite to what they were actually being show-cased by her or presented for them, to give a report on wherever they went to outside the homestead, and into other villages and houses alike.

One day in her own "*ot*" (house) after a large number of "*welo*" (visitors) had come to the house and the first wife had been accorded great respect amongst the company that had visited Nyamgondho's home, it was very apparent that she was very jealous and was not as happy as she was supposed to be as she wanted to have played the role of the "*mikayi*" (first wife) rather than playing a second fiddle to another person or a bunch, or a group of other people or co-wives.

It was that very night while lying on her bed that she got lost into deep thought and went into a pensive mode, and a very pensive mode it was.

In as much as there was no one with her to witness her physical demeanor, one could not help denying the fact that she was actually not that much troubled by what she was jealous about, but only troubled as to how she can stop that person who was making her jealous from being or ceasing to exist at all so that she can be the bonafide "*mikayi*" first wife, and be accorded the "*luoro*" (respect) and all that comes with that title in the "*dala*" (homestead).

After about an hour or two of "*paro matut*" (serious thought) and serious consideration, a sudden twinkle came or rushed into her eye from nowhere, that showed or verified the fact that she had found a pragmatic or a practical long-term solution to the problem that would finally lead her to earn the honor and respect that was currently being enjoyed by Nyar Nam on the basis of her title rather than her.

With great levels of confidence or even an accentuated height of determination, she finally said in a heart that, *"Wang'ni to atieko Nyar Nam ma onge ng'ama ong'eyo, ma akaw telo e dalani githuon."* (This time round, I am going to finish or anihilate Nyar Nam in a way that no one knows, and I am going to get her title in this homestead by force!).

In fact she even stood up from the *"pien"* (sleeping mat) that she laid or slept on, and started to pace back-and-forth in the room like one who was working on the final touches of a great scheme or a masterpiece plan.

Great excitement entered her and several times she started throwing her fists in the air as if to box or punch someone or chatting with a "fake" somebody or adult in which she knew that she was going to win and not only win the fight, but also, bring a complete end to her problem with Nyar Nam.

Oh Yes! She was going to do this once and for all, and in fact, it was clear that she had plotted to kill or annihilate's Nyar Nam as a method of eliminating her from the "equation" that brought her *"mor mar ngimane"* (joy and happiness in her life), irrespective as to the wether it was corrupt or not legal, or ill-conceived, or devoid of any virtue, evil, or truly just or unfair, she made it clear in her tough-headed mind that she had to do it, and "*mapiyo piyo*" (as quickly as was possible).

Oh yes! Many are times when in her own personal life, if she could not solve a problem with somebody resulting from "*nyiego*" (jealousy) or jealous altitudes, she thought very much in her head of how to "*nego*" (kill) or eliminate that person completely in her life even if it meant doing it personally.

And in fact, it is believed that in her own "*gweng'gi*" (home area), there were many "*jogweng'*" (villagers) who believed that one or two women who had lost their lives in mysterious circumstances, had their "*tho*" (deaths) linked to her own doings or crafty endeavors; And, in those kinds of situations these women were "*ne laro kode dichuo mane ogombo*" (competing with her on the man that was of a choice).

It was at this point in this oration that Chief Leinad Ongoda's mind reeled back to many situations where he had found out that prominent politicians, quite a number of dignitaries especially in the economic domain or arena in the higher echelons of the society, painfully and sadly lost their life to their antagonists through a similar method of elimination that the second wife was currently crafting to deal with not only the "*mikayi*" (first wife) in this "*kend*" (marriage) but also in previous contested relationships.

However, the "*sigana*" (story) had to continue as Rieko, was very busy orating as well as focusing on how well to articulate the next scene in the story without loosing the much-needed detail of it from his memory.

Was it Nyar Nam's death that was looming? Or was it true that the second wife was only in the process of succeeding in laying out her very own "*mtego mar tho*" (death trap) without even knowing it?

Chapter 10.

*T*he interesting thing is that on that very morninng that Nyar Nam's first co-wife planned on carrying out her secret plot to eliminate Nyar Nam from her "equation of happiness", the cock-crow that woke Nyar Nam up from her sleep, to get out of her bed and prepare for her journey to the *"puodho"* (farm), was a cock-crow from a neighboring homestead and not from her homestead.

And, being the person that she was, always alert even at the wee hours of the morning, she was probably the only one who heard that cock-crow and correctly responded to its signal of getting ready to attend to the chores of the day as well as to not only attract the wealth that that day had to offer or promised, but also to lock it in in her *"dala"* (homestead) as much as she could in preparation for *"ndalo mar oro"* (days of drought).

When her first co-wife woke up, it was also at amongst the first cork-crows in the homestead and since she had planned to secretly follow Nyar Nam to that which she attended to every day, she immediately got out of her house, and as she stood by her door-way to gaze at Nyar Nam's hut, she could not belive that Nyar Nam was already out of her house and had gone to the farm!

She could not believe it at all and mumbled her thoughts under her breath in frustration saying that, *"To dhako ma oti atiya ni, ere kaka otegno kamae ma onyalo kata kwongo na chiewo okinyi ma osira wende kata ma onyango kamae?"* (How is it that an old woman like this, is so strong and even able to wake up earlier than me even at the earliest of sunrise or dawn?).

Because of her rash decision to striate herself upon her paths of malice and destruction, she did not take her time to "read in between the lines" and tread cautiously especially when she dealt with people who did things that are extra-ordinary, or even had miraculous methods of materializing results, and brought hope where there seemed to be no hope, or engaged in activities that inspired on even improved faith where there seemed to be no faith, or where the fire of the faith had dwindled terribly; And, even were extremely charitable in environments or situations that one would often not be charitable or find any surviving *"kodhi"* (seed) of charity planted on that "ground" of humanity.

As she continued to gaze at the front of Nyar Nam's hut, she went into a very pensive mood while entertaining the thought as to weather Nyar Nam had died or was seriously ill or something of that nature but this thought was only to linger for a short while in her mind as her eyes caught the images of Nyar Nam's footsteps from her door all the way to the gate disappearing into the path that passed by the gate of the homestead.

She consoled hereself for the "defeat" in waking up early by saying to herself that, *"En mana nikech amer gotieno, emomiyo Nyar Nam okwongona chiewo kawuono, nono, to daloye."* (It was just because I was drunk last night and that is why Nyar Nam woke up earlier than me, otherwise, I would have defeated her).

She quickly girded herself with her loins and carried an *"ojalo"* (machette) as well as *"kwer"* (digging hoe) and off she was out of the homestead and into the *"ndara"* (path) that winded out of the homesteads and eased into the *"puothe"* (farmlands) of the village.

She made haste with her feet in order to catch up with Nyar Nam if she could as it was going to be easier for her to strategize her surprise attack on her once and for all. She had decided never again will she play second-fiddle to anyone in her homestead and even if it meant eliminating her husband herself if need be.

As she watched the machette in her hands, she said to herself in her mind that, "*Kawuono, ojalo ni okdhi duogo ot ka pok ochwero remo, ma onge ng'ama ne tug koda kendo e dala kae.*" (Today, this machette is not going to come back to my homestead before spilling some blood, and no one will ever "Lord" me again in my homestead).

She was very ambitious in her "*wuoth*" (travel) and had it been that she was not nursing a hung-over that morning, she would actually have "*goyo ng'wech*" (sprinted) all the way until she caught up with Nyar Nam.

One thing that depressed her and even frustated her to an epic degree, is that she can painfully recall that when she was a young' child, she was a very fast runner and even amongst the best in the "*gweng'*" (village) where she came from, but as she got into her late teens, she started to slack down in this hobby as she often found herself much more short of breath than even before, and hence she could not endure to the end that much in her marathons.

And in as much as she would have liked to deny it, she knew that it was because of her smoking habit that she had acquired or picked up from her *"dani"* (grandmother) who often smoked *"kwesi"* (pipe), and her parents turned a "blind eye" on this habit even when they should have done something responsible or positive about it.

It was after quite a while and after much *"reto"* (fast-walking), that she caught up with Nyar Nam, and she could see her at a distant up a hill as she was almost beginning to decend down that hill that they had to actually climb in order to reach their farms.

The travel to Nyamgondho's farmland *"ne ochwalore matin"* (was a little bit far) as they had to pass by *"puothe modongo dongo mane okwong' mak gi jotelo mag gweng' machon ndalo mane Nyamgondho pod odhier e gwen'no"* (large tracts of farmland that was first claimed by the elders of that village in the days when Nyamgondho was still a poor man in that village).

One interesting thing that caught the second wife's attention, is that even though she was quite a far and could barely see Nyar Nam ahead of her due to the lazy-but-uniquely-rude rays of the morning sun forcing themselves into her eyes, she could hear Nyar Nam singing and even clearly hear the words of the song as to even understand the song itself.

Amongst the words and sentences that she could pick up were as follows:

"Ruoth Nyasaye e jakwadha, ok anachand gimoro."

(The Lord is my shepherd; I shall not want.)

"Omiyo anindo e lum mang'ich, otelona e geng pige mokuwe,"

(He maketh me to lie down in green pastures: he leadeth me beside the still waters.)

"Oduogo chunya. Otaya e yore mag tim makare mondo nyinge oyud duong'."

(He restoreth my soul: he leadeth me in the paths of righteousness for his name's sake.)

"Kata bed ni awuotho e hoho mar tipo mar tho, to ok analuor gimoro marach, nimar in koda; ludhi gi mikwachigin ema gihoya."

(Yea, though I walk through the valley of the shadow of death, I will fear no evil: for thou art with me; thy rod and thy staff they comfort me.)

"Iiko mesa e nyima ka wasika neno. Iwiro wiya gi mo; okombena opong' moo oko."

(Thou preparest a table before me in the presence of mine enemies: thou anointest my head with oil; my cup runneth over.)

"Adier, ber gi hera biro siko ka luwo bang'a ndalo duto mag ngimana, kendo abiro dak e od Jehova nyaka chieng'."

(Surely goodness and mercy shall follow me all the days of my life: and I will dwell in the house of the Lord for ever.)

Now, it was true that in all her life, it was her first time hearing this song and as she tried to understand the message in it, she could not help to pose in her mind an open and candid question saying, *"Yawa dhakoni to wero ang'oni?"* (What is this woman singing?).

In as much as this question was rhetorical at first, later on that day, she would find out just a little bit who Nyar Nam really was, and even a scanty comprehension of the subject matter as well as the overriding theme of the message and power or potency of that song especially to they who meditated upon its words daily.

As she heard this song being chorused over and over again, she began to slow down in her pace towards Nyar Nam. It was her desire not to alert her of her presence as her tact was to catch her unawares and especially when no one was actually around to see her perform the slaughter of which could be later on be blamed from a stray marauding *"ondiek"* (hyena) or other wild animals that often strayed from the bushes from the otherwise thick forest sorrouding the fertile farmlands that yielded a variety of harvests in successive seasons.

She was slowing down in her pace for two reasons and one of them was that Nyar Nam may have secretly seen her on the way before she had noticed her presence and was equally planning a surprise attack at least for defense purposes.

Another reason that she couldn't deny even if she tried to do so, was the fact that the words from the song that Nyar Nam was singing over and over again, were actually "hitting" her and registering a real feeling of fear, retreat or even surrender on her part especially on her evil plot that she was absolutely determined to carry out.

Nyar Nam sung her song in pure Dholuo and repeated it over again in another language that she did not understand yet she could tell, feel or even sense that the message contained therein was the same.

Despite the hurdle to relent or retreat in her evil plot to anihilate Nyar Nam in private and away from the public's eye as much as is possible, she succeeded in ignoring the wise counsel contained in that song and determined to seek the relief that she was seeking and if need be, she may later on repent or *"kwayo ng'wono"* (ask for forgiveness) like many sinners erreouneously concluded whenever they felt their feet were lighter towards commiting a sin or a group of sins only to find out the very hard and painful way, that prevention is better than cure.

As, she decreased her pace, she decided in her mind that she was not going to pounce on Nyar Nam along the way as she sung this song, but would delay her attack when she had already gotten to her farmland and worked herself till she got tired and took a break in between morning and midday.

Only then, she would find it easier to attack her as, there would be no one present to witness this attack at that time, and she would be extremely tired and seated somewhere drinking her *"Nyuk kal"* (Sorghum porridge) and *"Rabuon"* (Sweet potatoes).

So she let Nyar Nam continue to walk until she was out of her site and as she continued to follow her footsteps, she planned on taking a nap in a nearby bush close to Nyar Nam's farm but concealed well enough for her not to be seen or detected or even her cover blown by the scarcity of the leaves in the bushes or thickets that she had chosen.

Even though she was evilspirited, Nyar Nam's first co-wife was a very calculating woman indeed. She even thought of the eventuality of her falling asleep in the bushes or thickets for a protracted period of time and being caught off-guard in her deep sleep, but she brushed such thoughts aside as she was not the snoring type like many other alcoholics in that day and time, and even today. Perhaps, being athletic and staying physically fit had something to do with it or so she thought.

It so happened that she actually arrived at her destination where Nyar Nam had already arrived earlier and was easing herself in the process of tilling the land in the best way that she knew and with great passion as she liked to *"puro"* (cultivate her land).

She carefully chose the best hiding spot in the area and treaded cautiously towards it for fear of being detected even by another passers-by if there was any. She was lucky to have found a spot where she could quickly lay down on the cool green grass that had carpeted the bushy area and provided a relatively comfortable place for anyone to lay down and rest their head especially in such circumstances.

As she lowered her body on the grass to lay down, she sincerely regreted that she had left her house in a rash and in as much as she was a calculating person, she did not forsee the fact that her plot or desire could be delayed in such a manner as had happened.

Because she had rushed into this decision, she found herself leaving her homestead without any food or at least a guard of "*pi modho*" (drinking water) to quench her thirst especially at this very hour when she needed some cool water not only for her dry throat, but also for the silencing of her terrible hangover. In as much as she was enraged, she calmed herself even as to fall asleep due to the fact that today, it will be all over between her and Nyar Nam.

It was not long before she started to sleep that deep sleep actually set in especially given the fact that she was still drunk. Nyar Nam continued with her cultivation of the land as usual and this day she was doing the *"doyo"* (weeding) of her precious and delicate *"pith"* (crops) that was not only the pride of the village, but was also the source of great delicasies for her family, relatives and friends as well especially during the time of great festivities, *"budho"* (gatherings) or occasions of symbolic or great repute as was generally accepted by the traditions of the people and securely captured in its rich history from generation to generation.

It was while relatively in the midddle of the *"puodho"* (farm), that all over sudden, Nyar Nam heard a very uncommon sound that could not be ignored or could not go unnoticed even for the untrained ears, emanating from the peripheries of the farm that she was attending to.

Even though, it was an uncommon sound in that area especially given the fact that she was there alone, it was obvious to anybody even to a toddler or child to pick up. However, one could not deny that that sound was quite alarming or shocking indeed and she could not ignore it at all lest it be the reason for one's fatality or a serious encounter with *"tho"* (death).

Chapter 11

*T*he noice was so loud that Nyar Nam immediatly dropped her *"kwer"* (Digging hoe or gardening tool) and focused her gaze towards the area in question and watched keenly at the happenings in that environment.

No sooner had she started looking in that direction and skillfully glancing at strategic points around her farm, that she had a similar noise emanating from tht bush again and again a couple times and then it slowly died out. While she had already made up her mind of what it was with absolute certaininty, she couldn't ignore the *"nyiero"* (laughter) that it brought to her mind even though she did not laugh loudly for a reason.

It was evident that there was a *"ng'ama ng'ongo"* (mature adult) hiding in that bush, and that adult was deep asleep and so much asleep that in as much as the person was not snoring, the person could not conceal their cover as they were consistently *"kwodho"* (farting) even without them knowing or noticing and hence, they could not conceal.

Nyar Nam quickly put "two and two" together and with her uncommon or mysterious wisdom, she already knew who was hiding in there and generally for what purpose. Even though she knew that it was her first co-wife, she could not help to laught inwardly in her mind as it is true that, *"Nyiekeno, ne okwuodho matek kabisa, kendo kwoth ma rabet miwuoro mana gi liyo."* (Her co-wife fart was so loud, and uniquely signature that anyone who heard it, would not ignore the surprise that it elicited).

Howevover, having been gifted in *"thieth"* (medicine or healing), Nyar Nam knew straight away, that her co-wife had a serious medical problem in her digestive system especially in her stomach. *"Ne en gi njofni e iye mane chiegni kelone two"* (She had worms in her stomach that were at a brink of attracting for her an illness or malady."

However, since she never woke up from her sleep, Nyar Nam did not even dare to more closer or inch towards that bush, but continued with her farm duties but now much more alert and being aware of the fact that she had company and that her life might now be in danger.

As she bent down to continue with her weeding, pang's of anger hit her as she struggled with emotions of *"mirima"* (anger), wondering why *"nyieke ma oonge godo gi wach lawe"* (her co-wife of whom she had no aggression towards, was plotting for her downfall or even death).

Even though such feelings were intense and could overpower someone and move them into deep thoughts of entertaining actions of *"chulo kwor"* (revenge), Nyar Nam was a different kind of person as she knew how to control her anger even in times of great tests.

However, as she continued to entertain such thoughts and ask her self retorical questions, she said affirmatively in her heart that, *"Mbwa hii ataniona leo"* (This dog will see me today....).

She was so annoyed by this scenario that she referred to her first co-wife as a *"guok or mbwa"* (dog) meaning that she was of loose morals. At this time also, in her thoughts, Nyar Nam remembered some wise counsel from a man of authority that she had once come across and taught her lots of wisdom and amongst his wise counsel was the words that, "A man without self-control, is like a broken vessel without no walls."

Several moments passed by as she continued with her farm duties normally and not worried at all as she not only knew that the defense she had, was no match for the assailant-to-be or the perpetrator-of-the-crime-to-be, but was also not neccessary to be used when the assailant was stil in deep slumber and was going to be in deep slumber for long.

However, while meditating on the wise counsel of the man of authority who taught about self-control, she often wondered why quite a number of people who had this similar counsel or advise, only focused on the first aspect of it while ignoring the secong part or aspect of the moral teaching as it was equally important to the first.

In other words, a broken city is bad enough to be compared to a man without self-control and would appear to the untrained eye or not-as-attentive ears, to suffice or be enough in ramifying or elucidating the point being stressed by the counselor or teacher; However, why does the same counselor or teacher continue to compare the man without self-control to not only a broken city, but also a broken city without no walls?

She also pondered on the fact, that had she been malicious or revengeful, would she not have already revenged on her first co-wife without anyone even knowing? And also, if her first co-wife was as daring as to go this far, what would stop her from even causing serious harm or even killing her husband, Nyamgondho?

Nyar Nam was saddened by the fact, that both Nyamgondho and her co-wives were victims to their lack of self-control or wreckless behavior and were open to very serious hazards especially from outsiders who were especially jealous of them or not so friendly or kind to their increasingly coveted status in their society.

Nyar Nam even went as far as wondering, what if they had their own children as they were planning on having, would they change for the better to be great examples for their children or kids to emulate, or will they continue their lifestyle in the same or similar fashion?

She was much more saddened by the *"nyao"* (laziness) especially of the first co-wife who was now just about to painfully realize, that there is never such a thing as a perfect crime, and however much she still thought so, she had a lot to learn especially from the traspirations of the events in this story as nature would determine for them to unfold one after the other, like the cascading of cards in a dominos game.

It was a few minutes past 10:00am that "*gokinyi*" (morning), when Nyar Nam decided to take a quick break from her duties in the farm and as the thought of having an "*aguata of nyuk kal*" (a calabash of sorghum porridge) and "*rabuon mosinji*" (sweet potatoes) crossed her mind, she almost simultaneously thought about changing her venue closed to her assailant-to-be as it was about time that she woke up or Nyar Nam would be forced to wake her up and tackle the matter as is similar to one that was taking the "bull by its horns", as this was the most appropriate thing to do, or mode of action to embrace given the dire circumstances as well as the level of security available and the time-frame available to react to this threat.

Now, Nyar Nam liked "*Nyuk kal*" (sorghum porridge) very much as it was famed for not only its dietary fibre, but also its natural ability to aid the human body in the control of "*adundo magwecho matek*" (High blood pressure), "*tuo sukari*" (Diabetes), cleaning and healing of clogged blood vessels, as well as providing the much-needed "*teko mang'eny*" (high energy) that she needed to complete her chores or labor-intensive tasks in the "*puodho*" (farm).

It was while preparing to eat that she also sympathized with young women on the dangers that many of them who rushed into being married to a *"jadoho"* (a man with many wives) faced and were not precautious about while entering their marriage; And, one of those dangers were like the one she faced today of insecurity inspired by *"nyiego, piem gi lawruok ei dala"* (jealousy and unhealthy competition in the homestead).

Almost immediately, another song came into her memory, and in as much as this song was sung in small play-like circles in the *"gwenge"* (villages) around by *"nyiri matindo"* (young girls) being taught by their *"deye"* (grandmothers) of the dangers of entering a plural marriage or insisting on being married by a *"jadoho"* (a man with many wives), this song became the most famous amongst these people of warning the young girls of the "lwenje madongo kendo malit manie ute mag doho" (very painful conflicts that existed in a polygamous homestead or a family of such a setting).

Some of the words and the lines of that song were as follows:

"Mayande waidho agola, mayande waidho agola"

(A while back, we used to use canoes; a while back, we used to use canoes)

"Sani waidho meli!, sani waidho meli!"

(Now we use boats!, now we use boats!)

"Wamenyo gi raha lilo, wamenyo gi raha lilo"

(We ply the waters with pure joy, we ply the waters with pure joy)

"Ayuni ni ehh!, Ayuni ni ehh!"

(Oh Ayuni!, Oh Ayuni!)

"Ayuni ni ehh!, ni ehh!, ni ehh!"

(Oh Ayuni!, Oh!, Oh!)

"Wuoru gi meru odagi"

(Your father and your mother have refused)

"Ni kik itedne jadhako"

(That you should not get married to a polygamous man)

"Dipokiyudo masira!"

(You may get into trouble!)

Ayuni was a proper noun as in, it was the name given to the proverbial young girl who was of marriage age and was being counseled to choose her marriage partner wisely, by avoiding the generally deadly traps of a polygamous marriage.

In fact, much later after several generations had passed in the Luo community, even caring fathers, especially those who survived the painful experiences of being born in a polygamous family or setting, were heard several times advising or counselling their daughters about considering joining a plural marriage by giving them a stern warning and telling them that, "*Tedo ne jadoho en hatari sana.*" (Getting married to a polygamous man is very dangerous).

And the often completed the conversation by ending it with these words, "*Tang' kabisa nyara, dipok iyudo masira.*" (Be very careful my daughter, you may get into trouble).

As she cleaned her clothing to remove the soil that had gathered on her in order to eat, she almost simoultaneously stamped her feet on the ground not because of anger or anytnig like that, but merely to shed off the dust and some mud that was still stuck on them.

Even though she was working in the farm, Nyar Nam was generally a very clean, neat and tidy person even in her "*tok dala*" (back of the homestead) that was often famed to be the "*molil ahinya*" (dirtiest or filthiest) or even the most ignored part of many homesteads.

In fact, in Nyar Nam's homestead, compost pits were dug well and deep enough to safely handle the waste or garbage that emmanated from the regular or normal activities including the occasions and festivities held or venued in the homestead as they came in the course of the passing seasons.

Although it wasn't her regular or favorite place to take a break when she was at the farm, she chose the bottom of this "*yien*" (tree) to "*yweyo*" (rest) on not only because its "*oboke*" (leaves) and branches formed an excellent canopy for the otherwise intensifying heat of the sun, but also because of its close proximity to where her first co-wife had decided to hide or seek a secret cover unknown to no one else under the sun or moon except her.

She poured her favorite "*nyuk Kal*" (sorghum porridge) from the gourd into the "*aguata*" (calabash), as well as serving herself a bounty of "*rabuon mosinji*" (baked sweet potatoes) and it didn't take long before she dived into this healthy delicacy with great relish after giving thanks to her God for the meal.

The peaceful and tranquil environment that existed in that area, was one of the favorite attractions of Nyar Nam to her farmlands. The regular and sometimes occasional whistling of a variety of "*winje*" birds passing by in their day-to-day activities depending on the seasons of the land or their periods of migration, provided the much-needed healing melodies that she treasured the most especially after a day or night of commotion or domestic rows that reared their "ugly heads" in her homestead often after excessive consumption of alcohol by her co-wives and their other family members.

The tall and majestic "*ng'ou*" (Baobab tree) that affixed itself confidently in her farmland, provided an elegant sight worth spectating, and often inspired her never to relent in her leadership responsibilities in her homestead however trying the circumstances may be. If a "*ng'ou*" (Baobab tree) or similar flora of the land could withstand the weathering of all storms even for over a century, who was man to give up in life?

In many of her decision-making or long-term strategic planning, she had confirmed over and over again through experience, that careful processing of relevant information required one to meditate upon their thoughts first before even speaking them out, as rash decisions made especially when they impacted the lives of other people, were often deadly or painfully costly in the long-run to both the decision-maker as well as the ones for which such decisions were made for. This was a pragmatic reality or a practical truth that many chiefs in different *"gwenge"* or villages around, found out the hard way.

Nyar Nam managed to complete her meal peacefully without any interruptions and after drinking some water and *"jier"* (belching), she reached for her *"ludh arungu"* (a club-like walking stick) to aid her in standing up as she desired to climb up a nearby *"lwanda maduong'"* (big rock) to *"oyo chieng'"* (bask in the sun).

One of the reasons as to why she aided herself with a club-like walking stick in her travels to the farm, is that every so often, a farmer would come across a stray *"thuol"* snake or some other *"le"* wild animals while going through their day-to-day activities in the farm and such a stick would come in handy especially for protection purposes.

Also, because of their being a poikilothermic animal, it was normal for snakes to climb up the same rocks or similar rocks in search for warmth in their reptilian bodies that were not designed to maintain a constant body temperature as was the case in human beings and all mammals alike.

As she confidently affixed herself on the huge and majestic grey-colored "*luanda*" or big rock, she enjoyed its warmth, and the main issue that lingered in her mind the most or captivated her audience more than anything else, is as to the reason as to why whoever was sleeping in the bush had not yet woke up or even showed more signs of life live alone the signs of well-being or normal health.

Chapter 12

*H*owever, as she glanced in the direction of the bush in question, she could start to hear some groaning and even occasional farting but for long and intermittent periods. In as much as the nature, rate and loudness of the farting could easily elicit some laughter and be taken as a thing or episode of comedy, she did not go in that direction at all as she was a *"jathieth mang'ongo e gweng"* (A reputed traditional healer or herbalist in the village).

As she looked at her co-wife struggling to stand up from her already-blown cover area, Nyar Nam mubled herself these words, *"Dhakoni iye rach kendo chando kabisa"* (This woman is seriously sick in the stomach and it is bothering her). Interestingly enough, when the first co-wife rose from the bush, the direction of her gaze was almost opposite of the direction in which Nyar Nam was seated and looking at her.

In other words, Nyar Nam was looking at her from the back and having known that her co-wife had actually hid herself upto this point, she did not utter any noise to distract her attention as she was also curious to see her reactions to her unexpected presence as well as hear from her on the nature of her unique visit.

The first co-wife struggled to stand upright given the fact that she had been drunk the previous night and honestly speaking, did not remember quite quickly as to the last day that she had been sober in the recent past.

She yawned while holding her right hand over her mouth and almost caughed a loud but as if to quickly remember that she was still under cover, she quickly suppressed her caugh while looking around as to see if there was anyone around or in her immediate vicinity, and to her utter dismay, she discovered that which she had feared the most in this evil plot. The "*fuolo*" (caughs) kept on coming involuntarily, and were not the type that could be suppressed or whose sounds could be muffled.

As she struggled between her now-loud caughs, her eyes could no longer ignore the eyes of Nyar Nam who was now looking at her *"tir"* (straight) and wavered not from her body and whatever she held in her hands. It was when their eyes locked *"wang-gi-wang"* (eye-to-eye) that the first co-wife uttered the words, *"Mayie yawa!"* (Oh my God!).

Now there are times when Nyar Nam had caught her unawares coming home late and sneaking back into the homestead after creeping out in the wee hours of the night to *"bayo mar chode ma siri"* (going to sleep around or mess with other men in secret), but Nyar Nam had never raised that issue up with Nyamgondho as Nyamgondho was also of a similar type.

But this time round, it was only the two of them and it was day-time, and there was no *"dichuo"* (man) around for her to pretend that she had been having some company.

It was definate that she had to explain herself and even *"lero wach maler"* (explain herself clearly) as she had strayed into Nyar Nam's farm without any express permission or notice despite the fact that she had her own farmland to attend to.

She quickly composed herself and while clearing her voice, she kindly greeted Nyar Nam, *"Oyawre ahinya nyieka! Idhi nade?"* (Good morning my co-wife! How are you doing?). Nyar Nam quickly responded by saying, *"In bende oyawre ahinya, adhi maber. Bita in?"* (Good morning to you also. I am doing fine. How about you?).

Being a pathological liar and a good one for that matter, she quickly cooked up a make-believe story to explain her being there unannounced and even in the most strange of circumstances.

Upon clearing her throat, she quickly but confidenty responded by saying, *"An bende ne achiewo ka iya ok ber. Iya osechanda ndalo mogwaro sanie, ma kane achiewo, to atemo manyi mondo akwayi ka in gi yienn ma nyalo thiedha. To kane aduong'o dhoodi, to ayudo ka ne isewuok okinyi ma osirawende ma koro nyaka ne aluwi aluwa nyaka e puodho mondo ayud kony nikuop, kawuono to iya ne okaya mokalo ma aparo kata ni anyalo sim."* (I woke up today not feeling well in my stomach. And my stomach has been aching for several days now. And when I woke up this morning, I knocked at your door to get some medication, but you were already, out of the hut headed towards the farm. It was then that I decided to follow you to the farm here because today, my stomach is aching more terribly than before, and I thought that I could even faint).

At this point, her right hand was already holding her belly close to her navel while her left hand was carrying the machette that she accompanied herself with. She faked an almost-believable sound that could convince almost anyone that was not skilled in such matters or was not experienced in such situations, to believe her otherwise "white" lie.

But Nyar Nam, being the person that she was and having fore-sight that was known to be unparalled even amongst equals, did not argue with her or rebuke her for her lie right there and then as she knew better ways to handle such matters amicably.

However, the first question that she asked her was as to why she did not carry with herself *"pi modho"* (drinking water) when she decided to come this far and could not wait for this matter to be solved at home when she returned.

While she tried to concort or cook up another *"miriambo"* (lie), Nyar Nam quickly saved her *"wich kuot"* (shame and embarassment) by quickly asking her to move closer to her so that she could physically be examined as a physician would to a patient.

As she cautiousy moved towards where Nyar Nam was seated atop the big rock, she faked a limp that was sinonymous with one who is sick in the stomach and even though she was to be one in such pain and agony that demanded urgent or almost immediate attention, she still held her *"ojalo"* (machette) in her left hand now as she strode towards Nyar Nam.

She continued to talk or create a convincing conversation with Nyar Nam saying, *"Iya ni to osechanda ndalo mang'eny to yath makech ema asebedo ka aluoro ndalo gi duto."* (My stomach has been ailing me for quite a while now however, it is the bitterness of the medicinal herbs that I have been afraid of or been avoiding all these days…).

Before she could finish, Nyar Nam quickly interjected and told her, *"Ah, to donge kong'o ma umadhogaka donge bende ginbende gikech akecha?"* (Ah, but isn't it true that the alcohol that you and your drinking buddies often consume, are also bitter too?).

And before she could respond, Nyar Nam continued to add, *"Kendo aparo ni bende nitiere kong'o moko makech kabisa moloyo kata mana yath mochwaki mar adieri. Koso ariambo?"* (And, I think that there are some types of alcohol that are even more bitter than true herbal medicine that has been processed correctly even through boiling. Or am I lying?).

The first co-wife hesitated for a few moments while pretending to be focused on her limping walk and calculated slow-but-sure strides towards Nyar Nam's sitting place. At some point, she stopped walking after coming quite close to the "*lwanda*" (big rock) that Nyar Nam was sitting on creating an impression that she was experiencing some shortness of breath or something like that.

But having been alert of some impending danger from the word go, Nyar Nam did not make any point to move from her affixed position on that big grey rock that was quite signature indeed in that environment.

As the first co-wife noticed that Nyar Nam was not going to come down from her high seat on the big rock, she began to "*ng'unyo*" (mumble) some words beneath her breath as if to respond to Nyar Nam's earlier inquiry about the bitterness of medicine in comparison to the alcohol that she consumed regularly and even as recent as last night.

In as much as she passed about as an old, humble woman of a peaceful character and sometimes would be taken to be even foolish amongst they who had not known her, whenever such occasions arose, and scenarios where one was trying to conceal truth from her, Nyar Nam had such methods of rhetorical questioning that was geared towards proving to the liar that she was not buying their arguments or responses at all or at least some parts or fractions of their arguments or answers to such questions.

However, it was interesting to note how her first co-wife responded to her inquiry as she did not actually answer the questions posed unto her, but she thought of another way of diverting attention on this seemingly urgent matter, to another issue related to this one that seemed relevant to talk on even though it was not that much a priority.

While it was not as obvious to an honest audience or a sincere spectator, it was clear to anyone who had the skill-set of reading in between the lines, that all that the first co-wife was doing was buying time and strategizing herself to pounce on Nyar Nam as firmly and as sure as she could and with all her might and remaining strength.

From her position, the first co-wife began to ask Nyar Nam, "*Bende nitiere yath kata yiende ma anyalo thiedhragodo moloyo makechgi?*" (Is there medication or a set of medicine that I can use for my stomach problem that is not bitter like these ones that I know of?".

After getting into a pensive mood and giving this question a thought while looking into the direction of the "*chieng'*" sun, Nyar Nam finally had an answer for her, and she replied by saying, "*Yiendego nitiere mang'eny e kor pinyni to lakini nyaka koro iwuothi.*" (Such medicine are there and available in plenty around this world, however, you will have to travel in order to get them).

There was some excitement in the first co-wife's voice when she suddenly responded by saying, "*Adieri?*" (Is that really true?). Nyar Nam responded by saying, "En adieri kabisa" (Very much true). Nyar Nam continued by saying that, "*To yudo yiendego chuno ni nyaka iwuothi mabor kabisa e pinje mochwalore gi kuma wadakieni.*" (And finding such medicine will require or force you to travel far and distant into lands that are quite a distance from our village).

Despite being discouraged to travel in the search of such medicine at the moment, her co-wife was adamant and insisted on knowing more about this by saying, "*An ayie dhi kuno kata debedni bor manade.*" (I accept to travel to such distant lands however far they may be!).

In her own analysis or calculations, the first co-wife thought of the time frames that would elapse in one's travel back and forth to such distant lands and even the different weather conditions that the traveler can be subjected to in the course of their journey.

On the basis of her understanding of herbal medicine to be composed mostly of roots, tree branches and leaves, she concluded that it may not be that much possible to transport such medicine successfully from their source to their destination without some of them either perishing or even loosing their medical potency upon arrival or even at the time of use.

However, being the unrelenting or unyielding person that she was, another brilliant idea came into her mind and she thought about sharing it with Nyar Nam mainly for the thrill it gave her as well as buying ample time to gather strength for her next move.

She quickly asked Nyar Nam, "*Ang'eyo ni ting'o yath koa e pinje mabochogo nyaka e gweng'wa kae, en lweny mang'ongo ahinya kendo yiendego nyalo kethore e kor yo makel mirima kabisa kuom jathieth kod jatuo bende*" (I know that carrying such herbal medicine from such distant lands to our village can be such a daunting task and may require Herculian efforts from the messenger; And, such medicine can decay, rot or decompose while still on transit and this scenario can elicit a lot of anger or can be very annoying to both the medicineman and the patient).

She paused a little bit before suggesting her solutions. "To ka adhi kata awuotho e pinje maboyogo ma ayudo yiendego, kar mondo ating' obokegi, tok yiendego kata mana tie yiendego, to ating' mana kodhigi kende!" (What if I went or traveled to such distant lands and found the herbal medicine that to you are talking about, and then instead of carrying back their leaves, barks of the plants or trees, or even the roots of these medicinal plants, I would just carry back their seeds!).

While listening to her, Nyar Nam was surprised about her creativity and spontaneous responses to other people's questions or even inquiries. While seeing that she had captivated Nyar Nam's attention for a while, she quickly added by saying emphatically, "*Eh! Ka asechopo kodgi kae, to apidhogi to bang' gisechiek to ausogi kendo alosogodo mwandu mathoth!*" (Oh Yes! Once I get back with them here in our village, then I can plant them, and once they are ready for harvesting, I can harvest them and even sell them for a profit and get rich!).

Nyar Nam almost started laughing upon hearing such ambitions, but did not laugh at all as she realized that all this extended talk and the show that she was putting on was geared towards or meant to side-track her from focusing on her safety or security which was very much at stake here.

With the main aim or goal of shortening this conversation and focusing or directing attention to the first co-wife's stomach which was currently aching, Nyar Nam quickly replied to her by saying, "*Yiende moko ok nyal ti e lobni nikuop, kit lobwa opogore kod kit lowo mamoko, kendo chue mar koth kod rieny mar chieng' opogore e thuchego. En mana yien achiel ka chiel ema nyalo ti e lobwa kae, to be mana ka ing'eyo pidhe.*" (Some of those medicinal plants cannot thrive on our lands as our soils do not support their lives; And also, the rainy seasons and the nature of sunshine in those geographical regions are different from ours. Only a few can grow in our soils here in the village, and only if you know how to plant and take care of them).

It was then that after making these remarks in a polite tone, that Nyar Nam immediately pointed to her stomach with her body language changing to support the fact that she was not focused on the side-tracking of conversation and was ready to deal with the subject matter at hand or the main agenda in question.

As the first co-wife so that Nyar Nam had strategized to overpower her yet she was still regaining her strength, she intentionally and rudely ignored Nyar Nam's interjection and went back to the same topic as before by asking her, *"To gin yien mage ma kothgi nyalo ti e lopwa kae kata e gweng'wa kae?"* (And which medicinal herbs are they, whose seeds can grow or germinate in the soils here in our village?).

Although annoyed about this turn of events, Nyar Nam did not hesitate to reply to her question promptly and told her, *"Achiel kuomgi iluongo ni Moringa, to Moro bende iluongo ni Garcinia Cambogia, to moro bende en..."* (One of them is called Moringa, another one is called Garcinia Cambogia, and another one is called...). No sooner had she finished mentioning the names of these two medicinal plants whose potency in the medical field have stood the test of time, that the first co-wife made a very sharp, drastic and surprisingly dangerous move towards Nyar Nam!

Chapter 13

Surprisingly enough, Nyar Nam did not even move an inch from her sitting position atop that big, gray and majestic *"luanda"* (rock) and instead swiftly or quickly reached for her *"ludh-arungu"* (club-like walking stick) in a similar fashion as an archer would swiftly reach out for an arrow in his quiver and quickly mount it on his bow whenever he or she had to face or tackle an impending danger, or even a sharp shooter reaching for his or her gun whenever the call for duty arose especially if that call was spontenous or even instanteneous.

This lack of expected movement from Nyar Nam, really surprised her first cowife and she immediately sprung to her feet as if she was no longer sick and with her *"ojalo mabith kabisa"* (a very sharp machette), she charged towards Nyar Nam with *"mirima kabisa"* (seething anger) tearing down her body, and uttering these words aloud, *"Dhako ma raura ni!"* (This mad woman!) she started.

"Kawuono en kawuono! Adwaro tieki kae kae dakika! kendo ka diemo wang' ma akunyi e bur mopondo gi kweri no, ma onge ng'ama ne ne rembi kata matin!" (Today is today! I wanna finish you in the wink of an eye! and burry you in a secret grave where no one will ever see a drop or a trace of your blood ever!). And this time she did not mind her tone of voice at all, or how far her voice projected, or the direction in which the wind voyaged or set her message to travel in.

She continued further in a very angry tone and frothing in her mouth while saying out aloud, *"Iola gi weche magalagala mag dimbruok e dalanakae ma aonge kata gi raha kata matin!"* (You have tired me down with your house-keeping rules in my homestead with your consistent church-like mannerisms and traditions that I do not even have fun at all!"

And as if concluding her talk, she said *"Wang'ni an e mikayi e dalani ma onge ng'ama neloya kendo kata chika kendo..."* (This time round, I am the first wife in this homestead and no one ever will defeat me or rule over me...) And the finality in her voice was such as Nyar Nam had never ever heard from her before.

As she was finishing these words, she had already started to climb the big rock that Nyar Nam was sitting on but her haste or hurring, had prevented her from successfully climbing up in her first attempt as she fell down and was trying again.

In all this time, her blood-shot alcoholic eyes did not stray from looking *"tir"* (straight) at Nyar Nam's eyes even though it was a behaviour that was almost forbidden and greatly discouraged by the norms and the traditions of that society or culture in general.

It was while looking at Nyar Nam *"tir"* (straight) in the eyes, that she suddenly so Nyar Nam's *"ludh arungu"* (club-like walking stick, suddenly turn into an *"asere mabith kabisa"* (very sharp arrow).

The surprise in her face coupled with the fright in her body could not be hidden even if she tried to. Even though she wanted to *"goyo nduru"* (scream out aloud), her energy levels had gone down considerably and almost in an instant, and as she pondered on what to do next, she was relieved that Nyar Nam did not aim the bow and arrow at her but to a different direction away from them all.

While wondering why Nyar Nam was taking this rather awkward action, she could not help to look at what Nyar Nam was looking at, and found it more strange when she so that her attention as well as the bow and arrow was focused on a tree that barely did not have that much *"oboke"* (leaves) on its branches but was significantly tall and took up a lot of space.

It was while she was looking at the tree and with the corners of her eye skillfully looking at the bow and arrow in Nyar Nam's hands that she so, *"mak ne"* (A mistery or scary experience that no else has ever thought of).

No sooner had Nyar Nam aimed her arrow towards the tree, that she suddenly released the arrow towards it, and as it was normal for one to look at where the arrow struck, it was surprising that as soon as that arrow hit the *"kor yien"* (stem of the tree), suddenly strange and very vivid *"polo"* (lightening) immediately pierced the otherwise peaceful almost-midday sky that had no promise of rain, storm or any other similar kind of precipitation.

It was *"mil polo miwuoro ma pok one e pinyno"* (lightening such as has never been seen before in that land).

"Koyo ne oringo mapiyo piyo e luhumbru" (Chills ran down quickly in the spine) of the first cowife *"mane otetni kabisa ka luoro omake kabisa"* (And she trembled seriously with great fear); And, in as much as she could deny many things, one thing that she couldn't deny is that the alcohol in her body or

blood system, was completely gone, and she sincerely felt like diarhhoeaing without any question.

As she attempted to rapidly digest these *"midhiero"* (mysterious events) as well as the once-secure but now-turned insecure environment that she found herself in, some of her fears were confirmed when the lightening was almost followed with an overwhelmingly loud and scary *"riadruok mar polo"* (thunderbolt) that hit the tree while forcing her to *"dieo"* (diarrhoea) instantly *"e kor odiechieng e wang' lela!"* (in broad daylight and in public!).

"Polo ne oriadorene malich ahinya e dier kochieng tir mana kaka ne ong'iyo wang Nyar Nam tir maonge gi luoro". (The thunder and lightening was very terrible and uniquely signature as well as mysterious, and the lightening flushed in her eyes in a similar fashion as to how she had disrespectfully looked at Nyar Nam's eyes in her previous conversations.).

Apart from diarrhoerring almost immediately, the first cowife, had suddenly lost her balance when the thunderbold struck the tree, and to her utter dismay, the tree was seriously being consumed by the ravaging fire from the thunderbolt and headed towards her courtesy of the prevailing wind at that time!

Her once-famed strong body immediately felt like standing up and fleeing, but her body could not allow her as she had lost a lot of strength and was franctically gasping for air. Her gasping for air was not that much due to her falling down as well as the apparent shock of the strangeness of these occurences, but also due to the fact that she was now lying in a pool of diarrhoea that was truly stinking or offensive in its smell.

She honestly felt like throwing up or vomiting but even as she struggled to do so, she had barely nothing in her stomach. As the reality of her helplessness and suddenly-increased level of insecurity began to hit her like pangs of hunger, she could not help but look up at where Nyar Nam was.

As she looked up on top of the *"lwanda"* (big rock) that Nyar Nam was previously sitting on, she so her now standing upright, tall and majestic as well as confident with herself even though she was visibly old.

Oh Yes! Nyar Nam was as fit as a fiddle and as she continued to look at her, she regreted as to why she had concieved this hate and malice-inspired idea especially to one who has not aggressed her at all.

In all the times that she had stared at Nyar Nam's eyes "*tir*" (straight in the eye), the famed and virile strength in her body and muscles boosted her ego to think that she could physically tackle her seemingly-old and frail body in a matter of "*diemo wang*" (seconds), and "*goye amen*" (wrestle her) to the ground almost effortlessly. However, this time round, while carefully looking at Nyar Nam straight in the eye, something was strikingly different, and it was not the fact that she was lying helpless and frail on the ground.

Chapter 14

$\mathcal{I}$t was obvious that the only eyeview that she could afford to have or manage to use in seeing anything worthwhile or relevant in her precarious circumstance, was a worm's eyeview of Nyar Nam.

All this time, Nyar Nam was standing on top of that big rock with her bow in her left hand and another sharp arrow in her right hand, as well as a quiver full of arrows strapped to her back. It was then that her first co-wife noticed for the first time that despite "*Dende te te te*" (all her body) looking or appearing "*moti*" (old) by all the definitions of old that she knew, her eyes looked and appeared very young and cheerfully youthful by all accounts of that word or whatever idea it evoked in the mind of any careful observer!

The fright in her, prevented her from continuing to gaze at Nyar Nam in that disrespectful way, but as she "*miyo wang'e*" (closed her eyes) in fright, one memory lingered in her mind the most and she could never forget it at all.

The memory was of the color of the pupils of Nyar Nam. Unlike the color of the pupils of the eyes of all the people that she had looked at straight in the eye appearing to be black or hazel, the color of the pupils of Nyar Nam's eyes were actually as blue as the color of the sky above her that enveloped her otherwise elegant and strikingly authoritative figure.

While still closing her eyes in fright and not knowing what was next for her, she said in her mind, "*Wololo yaye! Kawuono to aneno mak'ne! Nyaka kata kit wang' ma pok aneno nyaka nene mama nyuola!*" (Oh my God! Today, I have seen that which no one else has seen! Even a colour of the eyes that I have never seen before since my mama gave birth to me!).

In as much as she desired to "*goyo nduru matek*" (scream out aloud) to seek for help, she was cautious not to do so as she did not want to attract any attention from anyone for obvious reasons lest she fall a victim of mob justice and even be stoned to death by the "*jogweng'*" (villagers) who were known not to take kindly to such ill-inspired and evil-spirited behaviour especially to "*jodongo*" (older people) in the community.

However, it was impossible to close her eyes for much longer as she may find it hard to defend herself from any revengeful attacks from Nyar Nam if any. It was now her time to attack and defend herself if she wanted and all the odds were to her favor including the mysterious powers of supernature not understood and experienced for the very first time by the assailant.

As she cautiously opened her eyes, she so Nyar Nam still standing in the same position and looking down at her. Apparently as Nyar Nam looked tall to other people, her first co-wife couldn't believe that a straight look at her revealed that she was actually much *"nyadundo"* (shorter), than she appeared to be.

It was while entertaining such thoughts that the first co-wife heard Nyar Nam's authoritative voice speaking directly to her saying, *"Raurani!"* (Mad person!). The sharpness in her voice indicated that she was very annoyed or uniquely infuriated by her actions, and so she thought that she was headed for some unique level of punishment for her gravious mistake or offense.

However, Nyar Nam surprised her by changing the direction of the conversation to another destination that the first co-wife didn't think of, or could not have concieved of given her background of violence, deceit and wrath for enemies.

Nyar Nam continued, "*Nyieka.*" (My co-wife), "*Bedga ka ing'eyo ni gima jaduong' neno, nyathi matin kata ma pod rawera, sechemoko ok nyal neno, kata mana ka oidho e wi yien kata mana e wi yath moro amora.*" (As a rule of thumb, always remember that what an old man sees, a young person may not be able to see even if he climbs on top of a tree.). "*Da kine kaka koro kong'o osechako rundi?*" (Can't u see how alcoholism has began to wreck your brain or impair your mind?).

It was at this juncture that Chief Leinad Ongoda's mind reeled again to the experiences that he had witnessed amongst other people who came his way, and in his regular day-to-day activities especially when he was actively involved in corporate gorvenance as well as even in his early or formative years in his career, in which he dealt directly with people from different walks of life and sometimes even unique social backgrounds that required a case-by-case analysis in the finding out of pragmatic solutions to their disputes amongst themselves, and even the government or various legal jurisdictions that they found themselves bound to.

Although reputed as a great disciplinarian and a respecter of rules, guidelines, ordinances, regulations, legal codes, or on matters of law, Chief Leinad Ongoda learnt from the bad or nasty experiences of fellow colleagues in the various industries that he served in, that in as much as one wielded power over others and felt that they can engage in some corruption by abusing their powers in order to gain an unfair advantage over others whom they considered weaker or vulnerable to themselves, it was best to avoid bullying especially older or even more experienced people in this world even though one had power over them.

In fact, having been gifted with a relatively much longer life than quite a number of his colleagues in the field, Chief Leinad Ongoda had observed and could attest to the fact that the abuse of power or authority of one over the other even if such power or authority was not explitely spelt out in a rule book, or where such power existed but in an informal setting like a family or neigbohood, in the long-run, often brought to the abuser much more sorrow, grief, pain, great levels of shame and embarrassment even if it was not immeadiate.

This was often true in the cases of forced sexual activities esecially sexual harrassment in workplaces, schools, clubs, fraternities, sororities, neighborhoods and churches, as well as domestic violence especially in the privacy of one's home or homesteads as was the case here in the scenario between Nyar Nam and the first cowife.

The *"Jodongo"* (elders), or *"Jomoti"* (old people) had unique ways of protecting themselves and more often than not, such methods of self-defense or security employed very deadly or potent *"midhiero"* (mistery) or *"rieko mopandi"* (hidden wisdom).

Chief Leinad Ongoda made it not only his role, duty and obligation to educate and nurture his children and great grand children alike to always find it in their hearts to avoid the temptations of bullying others or promote the environments where bullying and attrittion between people was entertained. He ingrained in their mind the harsh reality that true peace anywhere in the world, was a function of barriers.

They knew very well that, if they did not have their own barriers based on moral truths that were bed-rocked or hinged on the high standard of universal, timeless and immutable laws of human behavior, then they were headed or bound to deal with very painful and often devastating calamities such as was experienced by the famous Titanic ship that although considered and famed as unwreakable or unbrakeable, actually got wrecked and sunk to be very bottom of the ocean in places or locations where some parts of it are still yet to be recovered to-date.

And this is why they had developed a great skill of listening and even taking notes on the parts of the conversations or story-telling episodes that they had with their Great Grandpa. With the marvels of modern-day technology, he had observed quite a number of them carrying in their hands a variety of video as well as voice-recording devices to aid them in not only capturing the events of the time, but locking in the essence or even what he would term or call, the spirit of the moments worth noting.

Even though he was tired and sleepy from the activities of the previous night in his homestead, Chief Leinad Ongoda did not want to miss even a single bit of Rieko's recollection of his story on Nyamgondho *"wuod"* (son of) Ombare, and so he quickly turned his attention back to the narrative.

Rieko continued in his narration saying, "As she started to utter a response, the first co-wife found herself vomiting and the *"ng'ok"* (vomit) stunk of alcohol. Almost immediately,

Nyar Nam looked at her with no-nonsense eyes and with a *"duol makwiny"* (stern voice) commanded her saying , *"Chak wuoth idok e dala mondo ipar anena malong'o gima otimore kae kawuono ni."* (Get on your feet and head back home, and think carefully about what has happened here today).

As soon as she heard these words, the first co-wife was greatly releaved of her fear of revenge and stress; And in fact, as soon as Nyar Nam's words fell on her ears and her non-revengeful decision sunk into the deepest-most recesses of her heart or bossom, she found this response much more of a "breath of fresh air" at that moment than even oxygen itself.

Without murmuring or uttering any careless word, she quickly got up despite the mess that she had created, got her belongings and got on her way out of the *"puodho"* (farm) as fast as she could. In as much as she had wanted to *"ringo"* (sprint), or *"reto"* (walk faster), the harsh reality was that she was humbled by her general body weakness and the greatest defeat of her lifetime to-date.

As she walked out of Nyar Nam's farm, *"pi wang malit'"* (tears of sorrow) welled up in her eyes as she, being the woman that she was, and one who always defeats her advesaries *"e wang' lela mok pingi"* (in broad daylight unopposed), was today actually defeated by not even a young person, but an old lady.

While she consoled herself that there was no one else to witness this scene or laugh at her, she still had a bone to pick with Nyar Nam; But, what she did not know or understand, was her mysterious nature and how to successfully handle scenario's such as she had been in today.

It was clear in her head that this battle was not yet over as yet, and she must restrategize as quickly as possible even if it meant to reclaim her covetious status or title of always being a "*jaloyo*" in any "*lweny*" (duel or battle) that she got into.

It was while she was walking up the "*thur*" (hill) towards her "*dala*" (home), that *another* "*paro manyien*" (fresh idea) struck her mind or "*nodonjo e wiye*" (got into her head) giving her a new reason to smile even though her hopes of success had been seriously dwindled.

Chapter 15

$\mathcal{I}$ t so happened that as soon as the first co-wife arrived at her homestead, she tactfullly reduced her pace of walking even more as she wanted to *"lidho"* (stealthfully) sneak herself inside the compound without anybody noticing that she had even left at all; And, this was for obvious reasons.

As she approached the front gate, she could immediately see one of her other co-wife spreading the *"piende mag nindo madongo"* (large sleeping hides) in the *"laro"* (front yard) of her *"ot"* (hut). Being *"jomer"* (alcoholics) of different levels or degrees, it was not uncommon for these women to *"layo"* (pass urine) or urinate in their beddings at night especially after a night of binge drinking.

The first co-wife quickly thought of the small gate in the back of the homestead that was rarely used but was useful especially when the *"gwen"* (free-range chicken) and *"chiae matindo"* (small domesticated animals) were returning home from their day of free-ranging in the grazing lands of the *"gweng'"* (village).

She quicky sneaked in while no one was seeing her and luckily enough, no one had knocked at her door either or made an inquiry of her whearabouts since she left her hut that morning. She knew this was true as the belongings in her hut had remained untouched all the time she was away.

As she breathed a sigh of great relief upon her return, it was obvious that she was uniquely exhausted and shamefuly dirty. Most of the defication on her body as well as the vomit on her face, had fallen off during her journey back to the homestead, however, the stench or smell from her body, was quite a concern.

She quickly got or fetched some water from the *"aguch pi mang'ongo"* (big water pot) and poured it in the relevant or approriate water vessel used for taking baths: And in the back of her hut, she took a quick shower unnoticed.

Upon returning into her hut, and drinking quite a bit of *"pi mang'ich"* (cool water), it came to the point where her frail body could hardly hold the *"aguata"* (calabash) in her hand as she was greatly in need of rest.

Her *"pien"* (sleeping hides) were still spread on the floor of her hut and as her eyes grew heavier with sleep, she made sure that she put the calabash in its rightful place before she eased herself on the mat to sleep.

Her sleep was not a light one as it was very clear that, *"dende ne obwok kabisa kuom gik ma midhiero mane oneno"* (her body had experienced unique shock from the mysteries that she had experienced), *"kendo ne dended onyosore kabisa."* (also, her body was extremely tired).

When she finally woke up, she felt much better than before however, the guilt in her coupled with the shame and embarassment that she had expeienced and was going to continue experiencing, bothered her even the most.

In as much as she could tell that Nyar Nam was going to forgive her, she did not quite know whether she was going to share this information with any other person upto and including their husband, Nyamgondho himself. She was now fully awake and very alert although nursing pangs of hunger.

She was very grateful that one of her other co-wives of which she had struck an elevated-status of friendship not that much as cowives sharing the same husband, but moreso as drinking buddies, knocked at her door to check on her.

Based on the norms of their friendship, she did not wait for her to repond to the knock on the door for her to enter the house, and as she got inside and her eyes fell on the first co-wife, and almost immediately, she was shocked to see her that way.

She asked her in an unsually inquisitve tone, *"Nyieka,"* (My co-wife), she started, *"Ma kawuono piny oruni e ot ni, koso bin ituo?"* (That today, you have been indoors the whole day! Are you sick?)

It was true that she was sincerely concerned about her well-being and was ready to do anything within her power to attend to her even if it meant travelling a long distance to *"pono yath"* (uproot medicinal herbs or roots) from the places or rare locations where they grew *"e thim"* (in the forest).

The first cowife responded to her by saying, *"Erokamano nyawegi. Chiewo ema ne achiewo ka iya mwora kabisa."* (Thank you, daughter of other people. It is just that I woke up today, with a very terrible stomach ache). She continued by saying, *"Kaluore gi kaka ne wamer nyoro, kongo ne pod ni e wiya mang'eny."* (And due to the drinks that we had last night, the alcohol was still in my system quite a bit."

She ended by saying, *"Ema omiyo aneno ni ayue ayuea kawuono ma ok angokni ka akwodo wiya e mbele ji."* (That is why I decided to stay inside and rest rather than wobble around drunkadly ashaming myself in public.).

They looked at each other and both laughed out aloud in their normal fashion. While roaring in laughter one after another and gales of laughter filling or renting the air, all off a sudden they heard a loud *"gimoro"* (thing) hit the ground loudly outside the hut, and they both halted in their loudness, and almost in unison, peeped out of the door that was still ajay to inquire of the nature of that *"koko"* (sound).

It was then that they so Nyar Nam passing by from her hut that was adjascent from the hut of the first cowife, and next to her was an *"adita mang'ongo"* (huge basket) that contained *"bando"* or *"oduma"* (maize or corn on the cobs).

It was clear that Nyar Nam had arrived back from the farm and had accompanied herself with a load of maize harvest, and as she laid the huge basket from her head and onto the ground, the basket hit the ground with a loud thud that reverberated around even as far as the insides of the hut where the cowives were engaged in deep conversation.

They both feared Nyar Nam and in as much as they continued their conversation, they cut out the *"nyiero madongo"* (huge laughters) and lowered their *"duol"* (tone) imitating the ways of *"joma odimbre"* (mannerful or respectful people).

It was then that this co-wife told the first co-wife that, *"Odiechieng, ne ok aneno ka iro mar kendo wuok e wi odi."* (At around luchtime, I didn't see the smoke of cooking fire emanating from your house). She continued, *"To koro, ne aparo ni idhi e puodho kawuono mana kaka Nyar Nam odhi, ma ok achunra biro duong'o dho odi"* (And so, I thought that you had gone to the farm just as Nyar Nam did and I didn't bother to check on you).

With a concerned face and a matching tone, she added *"To ka piny dhi yuso, to aneno ka bende ok itedo. Ema omiyo abiro limi."* (And when the sun was setting down, I also so that you hadn't cooked at all. And that is why I came to visit you). Upon saying these words, she immediately extended a helping hand by telling her that, *"Bi ichiem e oda kawuono.*

Asetedo!" (Come and have supper in my house today. It is already prepared!).

With the excitement in her voice and the demanding tone in her conversation as well, there was no way that the first cowife could deny this offer and especially if they were to maintain their close friendship,

In as much as she was not as sure as to whether her stomach was ready for the consumption of solid food, she nevertheless found comfort in maintaining company tonight with someone she knew other than Nyar Nam, and so without any questioning, she nodded her head in accepting to dine in her cowife's house.

They both waited for Nyar Nam to enter her hut before they hurriedly but quietly made a quick dash to the venue of the dinner or supper as none of them was looking for any lectures or talks or conversations that they considered unnecessary.

They were glad that they made it to their venue unnoticed and without any interruptions even though the silhouette of the sunset was still lingering in the immediate sky above, and the radiance of its rays were still powerful to the eye even though they were on their way to retiring for the day.

There were signs of great relief on the faces of both the co-wives as soon as they shut the door behind them when they entered the hut, and in as much as the first co-wife had been struggling with lack of appetite earlier, it was very apparent that the aromas emanating from the already-prepared meal before them, was not that which she could ignore at all.

As she gazed on the still-hot *"kuon maliet"* (Hot cornbread), served with *"rech motedi"* (steamed fish), *"alot mokiki"* (mixed vegetables), coupled with a *"puga"* (gourd) of *"chag adila"* (fermented milk), she concluded that the dinner was irresistible.

Now, *"chag adila"* (fermented milk) and generally milk products including but not limited to *"chak mopuo"* (milk processed in a gourd by regular or consistent shaking), and *"mor nyaluo"* (clarified butter or ghee), were amongst the favorite foods or snacks of choice for the first co-wife.

In fact, she was known to eat excessively large amounts of *"mor nyaluo"* (clarified butter or ghee) with *"kuon maliet"* (hot maizemeal or cornbread) alone. Mostly, due to the nature, style or manner of its consumption, some people, tribesmen or fellow members of the community, often referred to *"mor nyaluo"* as to *"mor ayudha."*

This was fundamentally or basically the reason as to why Nyar Nam did not bother fetching for her any medicine earlier on in the day when she was in the farm as she knew that all she needed to deal with her *"ich kach"* (stomach aches), was to slow down on her consumption of dairy products even thought it had become addictive to her.

It was really the excessive consumption of these dairy products that gave her a lot of *"kwodho"* (gas or fart) and *"dieo"* (diarrhea) or loose stool that left a shameful an embarrassing memory of her earlier on in the day.

It was at this point that Chief Leinad Ongoda remembered the wise counsel that he had over and over again given to his children and subsequent descendants on the dire need or value of avoiding the very painful or horrendous traps set by indulging in what some wise men had singled out and classified as the seven deadly sins; and, amongst them was gluttony. Others included Pride, Envy, Greed, Lust, Anger and Sloth or Laziness.

Chief Leinad Ongoda had observed that many parents especially in the affluent continent that he lived in, painfully lost their children or were dealing with the effects of lifestyle diseases in their homes simply because the wise counsel of gluttony was not heeded to, or completely ignored at the dinner or breakfast table especially when it came to the consumption of cheese which is also a milk or a dairy product.

The Chief was very grateful that at least his descendants remembered these wise teachings and internalized them knowing very well that prevention is better than cure. In fact, he was very amazed at what Rieko could remember or recall from this story of Nyamgondho (son of) wuod Ombare and he carefully listened as he continued with the narration.

Apart from just having their dinner or supper together, the two co-wives delight in communicating with one another was more of getting that time of *"goyo mbaka mag oyuma kod kuotho"* (gossiping and backbiting).

They were a perfect match for these kinds of association as their tastes and even some goals in socializing were strikingly similar; And, it was while in the heat or middle of such *"loso"* (conversations), that the host co-wife asked her guest, to open up to her on what really happened to her, or transpired in her life earlier on that day as she had noticed some questionable scratches on her body that were still fresh!

Chapter 16

$\mathcal{W}$ith tears welling in her eyes, the first co-wife offered to disclose to her the transpirations of that day in her life, but on conditions of deep secrecy even as to the same level or standard of secrecy that they had on other matters that were important but not as relevant to the agenda here.

As she disclosed to her the major events that took place in the farm one after the other, the first co-wife hinted several times in her talk, that she wanted to plot a *"chulo kuor"* (revenge) attack on Nyar Nam but she just didn't know how; And, even more, she didn't know how to handle her mysterious powers, or protect herself from their deadly and scary effects.

There was a protracted or noticeably longer period of silence in their conversation after the first co-wife had narrated her part of the story to her co-wife. Her co-wife sat with her legs *"ka okarore"* (ajar) on the floor with the upper part of her body resting on her hands which were also touching the ground on her backside as to offer firm support especially for her relatively wider and well-shaped chest area or blossom that was the resting place of her *"thuno madongo"* (large breasts).

Even though her eyes were confidently affixed on the floor, it was definate that she was also shocked somehow at these mysterious occurrences and especially Nyar Nam's unique supernatural powers or abilities that were not considered ordinary to any human by all standards.

It was obvious that *"gino me omako dhoge"* (this event shocked her). However, there was something unique that the first co-wife so in her while she was digesting this event that was rather unusual especially given the reality of such *"timbe ma hono"* (supernatural occurrences).

It was interesting to her that when she was narrating to her her horrific ordeal, she had maintained a facial expressiion that was rather consistent with one who in as much as such things were mysterious, shocking and scary, it nevertheless didn't scare her as much as she was scared and even instantenously urinated and even diarrhoead on her self almost instanteneously.

While she was pondering on this matter, her co-wife began to respond to her narrative or experience of her night-marish ordeal that actually took stage "*e kor odiechieng'*) (in broad daylight).

"*Nyieka*" (my cowife), she began, "*Gik minenogo, chal ni gin juok mokikore ahinya ma korgi kata tiendegi galagala miwuoro.*" (What you so and experienced, looks like some form of witchcraft or a mixed form of traditional magic whose roots are uniquely strange).

While scratching her head as if trying to solve a very difficult puzzle or rummaging through her head for some much-needed and timely answers, she proceeded by asking a rhetorical question saying, "*Kata kamano, ok ang'eyo gima omiyo Nyar Nam ne ok ochulo kuor ma onegi gi kanyo kanyo kata ka wang'chieng' pok opodho?*" (Even though this happened, I still do not know why Nyar Nam did not revenge at all and kill or finish you there and then, or even before sunset?).

She continued, "*Aseneno juok mang'eny korwa lakini, mano kende e gima odhiera e wachnie.*" (I have seen a lot of withcraft and traditional magical manifestations from my native village, however, the only thing that is still a mystery to me is the reason as to why Nyar Nam let you go scottfree).

Based on her answers, the first cowife quickly looked out of the door with the main aim of checking where the *"chieng'"* (sun) was in its process of *"podho"* (setting).

She quickly found out that it was already *"gotieno"* (night time), and in as much as *"piny ne olil kendo otimo mudho"* (the village was dark and one could barerly see through the darkness), it was still possible to manouvre around especially for one who had had prior experience in *"wuotho gotieno"* (walking in the dark) even for protracted periods of time or long distances like both of them, especially when they used to come back home very late at night from *"miel milao"* (night dances) in other *"gwenge"* (villages).

It was then that the first cowife concieved another plot in her mind in light on the information she had not gathered from her host today. The only main problem was that she had to collude with someone or some people in order to be successful in her mission. The major risk inloved in this was that, if one of the parties decided not to keep the secret, then her life would be devastated for life.

However, due to the seething anger underneath her breath, and her longing desire to revenge and claim back her title of champion of champions on any feud, quarell or fight, she did not hesitate to share this plan with her cowife here.

As she laid out the plan meticulousy in low tones, it was not a shocker to her, that even her cowife had been harboring similar desires of getting rid of Nyar Nam completely and enjoying the *"mwandu mathoth"* (large wealth) of Nyamgondho without any boundaries or answering to anybody even to themselves.

In this plan, it was decided that they consult an *"ajuoga"* (a witch or a wizard), and seek for mysterious powers to anihilate or finish Nyar Nam for good without anybody knowing it was them or even suspecting them of being the culprits, as the *"juok"* (magic) that they had decided or settled in using, was that which never left a physical trace of evidence.

As they completed their plans and swore to utmost secrecy amongst themselves, the first cowife began to wind up the meeting telling her host that, *"Koro in ma ing'eyo jojuokgo, kiny ka piny oru, ka wadhi moto, to wang' wabar mondo walimgi mondo watiek wachnie nyadichiel…"* (Now that you are the one who know these magicians, tomorrow when the sun rises, as we head out in search of firewood, we will make a detour and visit some of these magicians so that we can solve this problem once and for all..."

"To ka dhoge pok noe olwar" (And before she could complete her conclusory remarks,), her host sharply interjected by exclaiming, *"Eih! Ma bende in gima rito nyaka kiny?"* (Hey! Is this a matter that needs to wait till tomorrow?). She continued, *"Bende ing'eyo ni Nyar Nam nyalo tieki kata mano kawuono?"* (Don't you know that Nyar Nam can anihilate or get rid of you even before the night is over?).

Before the first cowife could even ponder, think or reflect on the matter, she quickly added, *"Ang'eyo ajuoga moro matek kabisa ma kiling' ling' e gweng' kae ma ok nindga mapiyo. Anyalo teri kuno sanie!"* (I know of another very powerful yet secretive magician here in our village and he never sleeps early. I can take you there now!).

She continued forcefully by saying, *"Eh! Ka wapondo ma ok onewa, wanyalo reto mapiyo piyo ma wa dhi ma waduogi ka Nyamgondho pok oya e bayone mar kong'o!"* (Oh yes! If we hide and sneak out unseen, we can hurry quickly to get there, and make haste on our way back, and make it to our homestead before Nyamgondho returns back from his drinking spree!).

One of the reasons as to why the host cowife was rushing this plot was not only because she was excited about pleasing her favorite co-wife, but also because deep down in her *"chunye"* (heart), she had desired to use the *"mwandu"* (wealth) of Nyamgondho as she pleased without any *"chike"* (rules) or *"ratiro"* (guidelines) as was often stipulated by Nyar Nam or the *"Mikayi"* (first wife).

"E wiye" (In her mind), she did not care about titles in the homestead or level of respect accorded to each wife or anything of that matter other than the riches or the untold wealth of historic proportions; And, this was her *"kithor mar wach"* (main motivation) and the overriding theme of the benefits that she got from being married into Nyamgondho's household or family.

Several historic moments of silence passed while the first cowife wrestled with risks and scenarios in her mind, but as the silence in the room begun to be noticiably loud, it didn't take long before their eyes locked together and demanded for an answer in the heat of the moment. The first cowife agreed to the plan and accepted to seize the moment to solve this problem once and for all.

They both nodded to each other in unison and the next step was to spring into action as there was no time to waste. She did not have to return to her hut right now as what she needed for this journey was already there in her host's house.

The food she had eaten gave her enough strength as well as the *"pi modho mokwe"* (cool drinking water) from the *"aguch pi"* (water pot) had rehydrated her previously dehydrated body not only due to alcohol, but also due to the immense *"dieo"* (diarrhoea) that she had experienced earlier on in the day.

It was agreed upon that any payment that the *"ajuoga"* (witch doctor) demanded today, was to be paid the following day or within several days after the deal has gone through and in secret while the cost being split halfway between both of them.

Upon arming themselves each with an *"ojalo"* (machette), it was the first co-wife who led the way out of the host's hut, through the *"rangach"* (gate) of the homestead and into the winding paths leading away from the homestead into *"mieche mamoko"* (other people's homesteads).

Once again, it was the fate of "There-is-no-perfect-crime" that befell her again and this time round, as she was careful and extremely cautious to watch all the front doors and make sure that their ways were clear, she forgot that the round huts that they lived in, was built with a *"ndiri"* (sitting place) all around them including the back, and sometimes it was not unusual for Nyar Nam to sit in the back of her hut *"ka oluoko tao mag chiemo"* (while washing the eating utensils).

This time round, Nyar Nam was seated on the back side of her hut as if she knew that the first co-wife whose hut was adjascent to her's, was embarrased to behold her presence especially after what she had attempted to do earlier on in the day.

While it was true that making an attempt on one's life was bad enough, it was also true that living with that person in the same homestead, compound or even in the same neighborhood was even worse.

If one member of the family had exhibited the animalistic character, instinct or behavior likened to a *"kwach"* (leopard), or *"thuol ma kwiri ne kech"* (a poisonous snake) or any other dangerous *"le"* (wild animal), it was a "red flag" in that family and even the entire *"gweng'"* (village) to be on the lookout or tread cautiously in their relationships with that person.

She had not sat behind her hut that long, when she suddenly so the two heads of her cowives walking side by side along the path that led away from the *"dala"* (homestead).

She almost immediately asked herself a rhetorical but relevant question in her mind saying under her breath, "To en wuoth madade to madhi kanye otieno sanie?" (And what is the nature of this journey, and where is the destination of their travel at this time of the night?).

She quickly craned her neck to see properly but it was necessary for her to stand up on her feet to take a proper glance and lo behold, it was not only her first cowife, but also another one again!

As she prepared to sit down in her *"ndiri"* (seating place) again, she could not help to exclaim while uttering the following words, *'Wololo! Wololo! wololo yaye! Mon gi dwaro tho kendgi ma onge ng'ama oterogie?"* (Wololo! Wololo! wololo yaye! These women are looking for death by themselves without anybody leading them towards it?).

Chapter 17

*A*s she so their heads moving away from the "*dala*" (homestead) and steadily disappearing into the paths of the "*gweng*" (village), she could not help or could not resist repeating the exclamations of "*Wololo yaye!*" as the act of engaging in "*juok kata timbe mag sihoho*" (witchcraft), was a very gravious one in the community and was even "*kwero*" (sacrilegious).

"*Kara dhakoni wiye Tek manade!*" (This woman is more of a tough-head than I thought of!). "*Kuma gidhieni, aneno ka ura osechimogi tir.*" (Wherever they are going to, I see madness or insanity entering their minds without fail). "*Kata kamano, we aweya gidhi nikech gidwaro.*" (Anyway, let them go because they have decided to go there, and it is their desire to do so). "*Makmana ka gidwogo, to gibironeno gima ne Ongong' kod Olweru ne oneno.*" (However, when they come back, they will surely regret their actions).

171

It so happened in the Luo culture, the phrase that involved Ongong' and Olweru, was a phrase that was used whenever someone needed to shout out a loud warning of the perils or dire circumstances, or even the unusually painful consequences that would befall one if they dared to proceed with the action or set of actions in question.

Ongong' and Olweru were mysterious and unknown animals that are claimed to be in non-existence today because of some irresponsible actions that they undertook that led to their demise and ultimate extinction from the entire face of the *"piny"* (earth).

Although angry and even annoyed beyond a level of what one could call normal, Nyar Nam found it wise to be quiet with these events to herself and the parties involved; And, this was mainly because of the nature of her husband to be quick to violence especially whenever he was drunk and full of anger, or ire or was already courting angst from another source of argument or *"dhap ohala"* (business tussle) from a different party.

She had predicted that if her husband, Nyamgondho, found out what her first co-wife had done, then all hell might break loose in that homestead costing someone's life, or the lives of other people, or even leading to members of the otherwise same family sustaining serious *"inyruok"* (injuries) or even attracting *"songa"* (long-term or lifetime permanent health conditions or disabilities).

In as much as Nyamgondho, was the head of a polygamous family, he had the habit of announcing which house he was going to have supper or dinner the day before it happened, and it was the norm, culture or way of life, or tradition and essentialy the responsibility of the *"mikayi"* (first wife), to always ensure that her house always had some "*chiemo motedi*" (prepared food) for her husband even if *"ne onindo oko"* (he spent the night somewhere).; And Nyar Nam was not an exception.

She had already cooked and ate her supper knowing that Nyamgondho had arranged for his evening meal somewhere else however, it was not out of the norm for him to come back home late at night and snack on something before he slept; And, so she left him a sizeable meal by the *"kendo"* (fireside) before she walked out of the house to relax while seated on the "*tok ot*" (back-side of her house).

Upon witnessing her first cowife and her accompaniment sneaking out of the homestead at this ungodly and perilous hour of the night, despite her being tired and sore from the farmwork that she had done during the day, she decided to delay her sleeping time and wait for them to come back to the homestead where she would at least catch them *"e wang' lela"* (red-handed) before she proceeded with other methods of dealing with this matter.

In as much as she had an unparalleled and even now-confirmed methods of employing violence to solve her disputes, her method of choice was always diplomacy first even if it meant employing a unique level of patience in the matter or waiting for a time-consuming important process to complete before passing judgement or springing to action. It was clear to all in the community who had known her well enough, that making rash decisions was not her style.

As she sat back on the *"ndiri"* (raised sitting area constructed with the house), she knew that she had a lot of waiting to do and in such situations or circumstances, Nyar Nam often resorted to deep positive thoughts of reflection into her past events with a responsible focus into not only her future, but also the future of her loved ones as well.

She always believed that he or she that does not learn from history, will not only have a rather challenging time with the present, and will often end up repeating the same mistakes as they who had suffered from them in the past.

One of her favorite wise sayings in the comminuty on this one, was the one that taught that, *"Chako chon ber moloyo dhi ka ajuoga."* (It is better to start one's solid or long-term preparations in life early rather than to consult a witch for some spiritual corruption in high places, or indulge in witchcraft that was known for attracting very painful or dire consequences in one's life in the long run including but not limited to disabilities or death at times).

But in as much as it was true that experience teaches fools, it was also a pragmatic or a practical fact that wisdom is an acquired trait and almost everyone or all, must have been a fool at sometime or in certain periods of their lives before a fresh enlightenment came forth in their lives whether it was through education of some kind, or straight-up harsh purnishments for wrongs done, or ills committed to other people especially when spouses or the acquisition, or even the disposal of some *"mwandu"* (material wealth) was involved in the equation, or factored into the metric of relevance.

It was a very interesting phenomenon to Nyar Nam and especially many *"jodongo mariek"* (wise old men and women), that quite a number of young men and women alike, did not know how to distinguish wisdom and intelligence; and, they often errored in labeling people in very wrong and sometimes very offensive ways.

In her discussions, she found out that one of the easiest and fastest ways to prove to someone that they were wrong about this issue, was to think about the opposites of the things that they were saying or the truths that they were defending. For example, if one who was intelligent claimed to be wise even though he or she was not, she would ask him or her to tell her the actual word that was the opposite of intelligent.

She would subsequently ask them to mention the actual word that was the opposite of wisdom, and then compare whether the two really meant the same thing. In her conversations relevant to this agenda, it was not uncommon for her to ask them to think for a moment or ponder on such phrases as "an intelligent fool" and many others as they focused on the right conclusions of the matters at hand.

Nyar Nam also knew a very profound aspect of opposites in things or nature that many people never even had an iota of idea that such facts ever existed. For example, if one would look at a source of light or gaze at it keenly for a while until they were convinced that they so light; would it be possible to define light if one did not have an idea of darkness?

Would it be possible to know that something was sweet if one did not have the idea of bitterness or sourness? Would it be possible to define, happiness, peace and joy if their opposites like sadness, sorrow, pain, and grief amongst others did not exist?

Upon arriving at logical conclusions on this matter, one may think that they are over with their analysis only to find out that there is more to it. If one had gotten to the level of defining things, then they may acquire an education that leads them to know all there is to know in a discipline or philosophy in life; And, even be prideful as a god of some sort that is unshakeable or unchallenged only to find out that just because one knew or knows everything there is to know, it does not neccessarily mean that that wich they know, is all there is to know.

If that was the case, would there be words like "undefined"? And if one would find the opposite of "undefined" to be "defined" then they would be correct in their logic; However, they would still grapple with the harsh realty of the fact that, they do not know the "undefine". and therefore, they do not know all there is to know even if they know everything that can be known.

Nyar Nam knew very well and understood completely that it is from the realm of the "undefined" that defination or that which can be defined came from or was deemed forth from; And that, there is that which is in existence and superior mainly because such "undefined" were not created, and from the "undefined" is where the creator of things exists, lives or emanates from.

She also knew a beautiful song in her Luoland or tribe, that captured the existence of these truths in very few but thought-provoking and awe-inspiring words that encouraged one to have respect or even the reverence of their God even if they were not as close to Him in their relationship for fear of His "*chwat malit*" (wrath or painful purnishments); And, that song was titled: "*Midhiero midhiech midhiero*" (Mystery of Mysteries).

In as much as she did not have time to think about these things right now even though she knew them, she always taught the absolute truth to they who desired to hear her or lent an ear to her counsel.

She always reminded them that as a rule of thumb, anywhere in which definition could be found, it should always be remembered that however much that knowledge or understanding exists in this field, there will always be the "unknown" or "undefined" that had to be approached with caution in character, or treated with respect and not neglected at all, or even provoked with irresponsible behavior.

As soon as Rieko reached this point in his narration and paused for a moment to drink a glass of water, Chief Leinad Ongoda knew that these teachings were really true and uniquely potent or powerful and if one would internalize them, then they were bound to definitely transform one positively in the direction of great success and respect in life both *"ei dala kod pinje mabocho"* (at home and abroad).

It was at this point that Chief Leinad Ongoda, recalled unto his memory the famous song of *"Midhiero midhiech midhiero"* (The mystery of mysteries) that Nyar Nam understood from their ancestry, as its message and the prayer in it, had transformed his life to a much better person than he was before he came across that song and meditated on its deeply profound message.

Rieko gulped his glass of water quickly as his tone started to give the indication that he was coming to an end of his narrative, and he had to hurry up before his fellow grandchildren commenced to move him out of the stage as they were also eager to give their own favorite narrative or a recollection of the stories that they heard from their great grandpa, and in their own words.

Upon sensing their heightened level of urgency, Rieko continued very quickly as he glanced on the big or gigantic clock in one of the walls in the room.

It was not that long into the night when the captivating scenery of the star-filled sky became her experience. As she gazed into the beautiful spectacle of a variety of constellations of the stars, it was definite that she not only found beauty in them, but also gazed at them for other purposes which was unique to her and her alone.

Even Nyamgondho himself, upon noticing how studious she was of the "*polo*" (skies), and the length of time she spent gazing or staring at them, he couldn't help to conclude that there was much more to know or even understand from and about the "*sulue*" (stars), the "*chieng'*"(sun), the "*dwe*" (moon) and the "*polo te*" (entire heavenly bodies) in general.

It was very interesting however that whenever they sat together outside their hut and gazed or spectated at the skies in general, upon sincerely inquiring from her on what she knew and understood about the heavens, she was more than ready to teach him but as she started to lay down unto him the foundational knowledge and understanding of the "*midhieche mag polo*" (the mysteries of the heavens), it wasn't long before he started drifting into deep slumber; And, it wasn't because she was boring or anything like that, but because of his excessive consumption of "*kong'o*" (alcohol).

However, on this particular night, Nyamgondho was not there in person and her top-priority was not only her safety in the homestead, but also the safety of all her cowives as well as the "*jotich*" (workers), and even neighbors in case of the "*dhao*" (feud) amongst them getting out of hand or loud and violent for that matter.

In her mind, she not only had an idea but had already known the fate of all her cowives even before the first day that they set their "*tielo*" (foot), on the "*laro mar dalane*" (in the grounds of her homestead). It was going to be a very painful lesson for them that, "*nyuomo jadhako en tich matek miwuoro ahinya.*" (getting married to a polygamous man, was a uniquely challenging relationship to manage).

Rieko posed for a noticable moment when he uttered such truths as earlier on in his life, he had lost a very close school friend, who was a victim of domestic violence as both him and his mom were shot dead after a violent-turned domestic row between his friend's mother, who was a concubine, and the actual legal wife of his friends father.

As he struggled to hold back his tears, he knew that he was almost done with his narrative and would have lots of time to deal with such emotions well enough offstage than on stage. However, it was very obvious that loosing a childhood friend was not an easy loss or emotion to go through especially alone; And, one of the greatest remedies in the grieving or healing process, was to share one's thoughts with trusted loved ones and avoid being alone.

It is during this time, that Chief Leinad Ongoda recalled to memory the words of counsel from a famous sacred text whose truths have not only stood the test of time, but have also weathered the storms of mortality even for such truths to be confidently held by many as timeless truths in different parts of the world with varying civilizations, traditions, cultures and ways of life in general.

The specific wise counsel in question was on the intimate relationships especially amongst adults, be they young adults or not; And, the text made it clear that, "*Kik igomb chi nyawadu.*" (Do not covet your neighbors wife). While this counsel was written verbatim for men, it was obvious that it also referred to women also, and warning them never to covet the husbands of their fellow women.

In his days and times, it was the observation of Chief Leinad Ongoda as well as many other seniors in the society, that most houses that were broken or where divorce had wrecked relationships, at the center of the foundational conflict between the actual man and woman involved, was an element of contravening, repudiating or totally ignoring the dictates of this counsel.

Due to the fact that he was trying not to miss the words of Rieko in his narrative, he quickly refocused his attention to him; And in as much as he wrestled with keeping his thoughts still, he managed to bridle his passions and left his own thoughts to wait for a moment.

Even though it was clear that she had lost herself into deep and much-needed thought, it was also very apparent that her body needed "*yweyo mar adieri*" (real rest) from her toil on the farm however, as fate would have it, she had to keep her eyebrows up for a while longer. It was either Nyamgondho showing up first coming back from his drinking spree, or her first cowife and her accomplice showing up first, or all of them showing up at the same time!

It was way late at night, just after midnight, when the moon and the stars were clearly shining up in the sky, when the first co-wife made it to her house, and despite seeing them arriving at the "*rangach*" (gate) and cautiously opening it, she did not interrupt them for obvious reasons.

As the first co-wife stealthily strode to her hut, Nyar Nam could easily tell from her wobbly walking, that she had either gotten drunk or high again. The first co-wife intentionally used stealth so as to avoid any conversations with Nyar Nam today as she timed her very late arrival after her sleeping time, but to her utter dismay, she was still awake.

Oh yes! Nyar Nam was wide awake and stood beside her hut skillfully enough not to be seen by her approaching first co-wife until she reached right in front of her door where she could not "*ringo*" (flee) easily when caught "*e wang' lela*" (red handed). And it so happened that just as Nyar Nam had planned on catching her red-handed, she managed to do so with striking accuracy.

As soon as she reached her door, Nyar Nam straightened her voice aloud enough for her to not only hear her, but to turn around and recognize her presence. As she turned around, it was with great "*bwok*" (shock) and to her utter dismay, that she beheld her presence.

It was true that with respect to the "*mbi*" (status and character) of Nyar Nam not only as the "*mikayi*" (first wife) but also as "*dhano*" (a person), "*Gikanyo kanyo kanyono, kuyo makende ne omake kendo ne oo e dende mana ka koth ma okbwogre.*" (Immediately, immense fear gripped her and spread all through her body like an unstoppable rain or downpour in a storm).

While amidst the panic, she exclaimed aloud, "*Mayie! Masira kindaki!*" (Oh my God! Tragedy should never be mentioned in vain!). She continued, "*Ma en masira manade?*" (What a tragedy this is!). She added, "*Ma e kaka omaka malit e wang' lela ka eka aa ywayo njaga!*" (I have been caught red-handed painfully right after smoking weed or marijuana!).

As Nyar Nam was hearing her exclamations, she quickly decided to sit right next to the door of her hut, and it was while sitting on her *"ndiri"* (raised sitting area around a traditional hut), that Nyar Nam called her in a firm but low voice as not to attract anyone's attention other than her as well as not wake anyone up who had already fallen asleep....

The first cowife could not believe that all these horrendous things were happening to her and she could not deny that she was guilty as charged on all the counts of offenses that could be leveled or blamed on her. Tears had now began rolling down her cheeks and she had now decided to kneel down in surrender for the first time ever in her life.

Upon taking a good look at her first and realizing that she was very intoxicated with marijuana, Nyar Nam began by directing a proding as well as a warning question to her, *"Nyieka! Bende ing'eyo Rieko mar oula?"* (My co-wife! Do you know the meaning of the wisdom of the flood?)

Chapter 18

*W*ith tears rolling down her face and her hands begging for mercy from her kneeling position, it was clear that she was indeed trapped, and her fate was totally or entirely at the mercy of Nyar Nam. There was nowhere to run or even hide as the best place to hide was in her house which was just behind her, but was obviously not a viable option for obvious reasons.

"Rieko mar oula" (The wisdom of the flood), was essentially a deep-rooted proverb amongst the Luo people, that was used every so often to send a warning signal to one who was making a grave miscalculation in their analysis of something, or an event, or even a project even though they were intelligent people.

It was also true that amongst the people in this culture, it was normal and customary for long-term strategic decisions even amongst close family members, to be made and agreed upon in a *"bura"* (meeting of the stakeholders); and whatever was decided upon in that meeting, was echoed to all the participants that were affected by the outcome of the meeting.

It was now very apparent that she was not going to be able to avoid responding to Nyar Nam's inquiry lest she face her wrath or risk experiencing the breaking of her *"kend"* (marriage) as well as having to live with the *"wichkuot"* (shame and embarrassment) that all her negative actions had brought unto her, or the truths that she had conveniently ignored.

As she rummaged in her brain in search of the right answer, the thoughts of the meaning of *"Rieko mar oula"* started to appear real to her today than they have never been before even when she had ample time for herself to ponder about such things as she truly loved to "loso" (talk).

As she struggled to recollect her senses amidst all these tragedies and unexpected turn of events, it was clear that the *"kong'o"* (alcohol) as well as the *"njaga"* (marijuana) in her system, was going to be evident in her speech in a way that could not be hidden however much she tried.

But in as much as she struggled with this practicality, she couldn't deny that in as much as she had known the proverb of "*rieko mar oula*", it was for the very first time that the harsh reality of its meaning sinked into the deepestmost recesses of her heart in ways that could never ever be erased in her entire life.

"*Oula*" meant "a flood" while "*rieko*" meant wisdom. Whenever it rained heavily and a flood formed from the highest-most parts of the terrain of the land or geography of the region to the lower-most parts of the land, and finally emptying its waters into a large water body which was often a nearby large part of a river or lake, one characteristic of the flood stood out consistently.

As the flood moved downwards from the hills or mountainous regions, they cannot help to respond to the demands of the force of gravity of the earth just like any other object or person would do whether they like it or not.

While in the process of travelling even from the top of a mountain to the lower parts of it, it is normal that human beings or animals even domesticated ones like chatel for example, often travelled smoothly, but when they hit a blockage on the road or some huge barrier on the path, the determination to proceed further often diminishes and even dies at that point.

In fact, even if there is a willingness to proceed further, the feet of the traveller or travellers often become heavier and there is a natural tendency to either quit or if it is a movement of migration, there is often a great natural tendency for the travellers to find out if that specific area has the resources necessary to support their survival or mode of life without bothering to move any further.

If they find out that the land in question is able to satisfy their demands and needs, then more often than not, that place becomes the new settlement area, or the new zone of comfort even though the original destination still remains in question, and the promise of getting to the the orignual destination may even be abandoned in the long run due to the challenges or impediments met on the way to that desired destination.

However, when it comes to floods, there was a unique nature or pattern of movement that was worth noting and learning from, and it is the essence of this overpowering nature of the flood, that forms the spirit of this proverb of "Rieko mar oula."

When a flood moves from the top of a mountain or a hilly region, there are points in its journey where it encounters great barriers or obstructions in its way, as it journeys down to a large water body which is its final resting area or the original destination of choice.

These obstacles can be very strange or hard to move over, or accross, or even under these barricades especially if they are hard rocks that are indigenous to that land or terrain, and are more of an igneous or metamorphic origin rather than sedimentary.

However, despite the barricades, blockages or the immense opposition that the flood faces, somehow, floods often manage to get going on their journey even if it means breaking the rocks, or carring alongside the loose houses or weak dwelling places affixed or built along their way, even killing and carrying huge wild animals that oppose its motion.

In fact, the flood would even use or leverage the moving or propelling forces of the objects or even the vegetation that it sweeps along its way, to aid in the breaking or denudating of huge rocks to make them relatively smaller and easier to flow with the flood rather than block its way.

Ultimately, even if it takes days or weeks or even any other noticeable or protracted period of time, the flood is observed to have steadily broke the record of that which upon setting on a journey, ultimately ends up achieving its goal of reaching to the final destination, and never giving up despite the unique challenges faced along the way.

However, what if the same flood upon reaching its final destination, finds out that it needs to climb up the terrain again or another different terrain in order to save its waters, will it be able to do so? When the flood is placed with the challenge of moving up against the force of gravitiy, can it succeed in retracing its steps as is often neccessary in the course of a normal life in this fallen world?

It is true, that when it comes to flowing downhill or gravitating towards its final destination from a period of high altitude to a period of low alitude, the wisdom of the flood is unrivalled, unparralled and even unquestionably superior.

It is also important to note however, that in as much as a flood posses this unquestionably superior wisdom and gets by with it, it can never backtrack or retrace its course even if it desires to; Hence, in the so-called "game of life", using or employing myopic systems or short-sighted problem-solving methods like "juok" (witchcraft), and relying on them for long-term pragmatic solutions in the real world, is bound to devastate not only an individuals life, but the lives of members of that "anyuola" (family) or "gweng'" (community) at large.

In fact, this is one of the few proverbs that is ended with a question mark with the main purpose of warning the members of the community not to embark or ever travel in the erroneous and uniquely tracherous direction of solving problems as the consequesnces are painfully dire even if they are not immediately felt.

The complete proverb was stated as follows: "*Oula uriek, to bende utwenyo got?*" (Oh ye floods, how intelligent you are! But can you climb up a mountain?).

It was a lot of thought as well as flashbacks for her as she recollected such truths from her memory when she was taught such traditions in her formative years of development or early youth.

She knew that at this point there were real as well as dire or painful consequences that she had to face due to her erronous choices in solving the problems in her heart or in amicably dealing with the internal conflicts in her life.

At this point, she even remembered Nyar Nam's wise counsel or teachings unto them one evening after dinner and seated outside of ther huts in the *"laro"* (open place infront of the doors of a house or hut), in which she tought all her cowives the core values and principles of life worth noting as well as embracing or examples worth emulating in life, and she did this freely as much as the time of that night would allow her.

And among's such teaching was the recognition of the harsh or even brutal reality that life on earth is a probationary place in which one cannot escape the endurance of pain in three major regions or aspects of their lives, irrespective of whether they are born with a silver-spoon in the mouth.

One of those categories of the endurance of pain was the tempations of the loss of or lack of a promising financial future that included the acquisition as well as the retention of that material wealth especially for the satisfacton of one's temporal needs.

The second category in the endurance of pain for humanity in general, was the temptations that one would endure as a result of the loss of, or the acquisition as well as the retention of our relationships with other people including but not limited to our intimate friends of which we romance with, our spouses, our siblings, our children and the entire neihborhood of all people that we interract with especially in our normal or regular day-to-day activities.

And she also remembered that the third category in the endurance of pain for humanity, was in the temptations that one would endure when dealing with *"two mar del kod wich"* (personal health issues be they physical or mental); And, it is in this category third category of the endurance of *"lit"* (pain), that she was dealing with right now.

The first cowife also remembered Nyar Nam saying that, that it was better to endure pain through disciplining of oneself in the ways or paths of righteousness, or else, endure pain in life through the suffering of consequences of one's unwise or foolish choices.

There was no doubt at all as it was apparent that at this point, she was enduring the immense pain in her body as well as her soul due to the consequences of her unwise, irresponsible, selfish, ulterior and even outrightly foolish choices.

All of a sudden, she so the shadow of Nyar Nam moving on the ground as the moon was so bright that night, and it was this moment that brought her back to the present and "now" of that time in which she was expected to respond to a valid question.

The shadow was cast when Nyar Nam was moving her "*lwete ma kor achwich*" (right hand) that had previously been resting on the right side of the "*ndiri*" that she was sitting on to holding her chin up in order to attract her first cowife's attention and skillful bring her back to the present.

The first cowife realized that quite a bit of time had passed by but as soon as she oppened her mouth to start talking, she smelt a very powerful and nauseating stench emanating from her guts and through her mouth as well as her nose causing her to vomit almost immediately.

Nyar Nam stayed sitted and not moving as she knew that this vomit was not a symptom of an illness, or a malady of great concern as it was due to the excessive consumption of "*kong'o*" (alcohol) as well as "*njaga*" (marijuana).

She threw up several times and then sat down as it was vividly clear that she had ran out of strength to kneel down as she had decided to exhibit her surrender.

The night was not getting younger at all and using her own wisdom and discression, Nyar Nam told her, "*Dhi nindi.*

Wabiro loso kiny." (Go and sleep, we will talk tomorrow). It was the wise thing to do given the scenario and her merciful character; After all, what wisdom was there in engaging in a constructive dialogue with someone whose judgement was already impaired by heavy indulgence in alcohol and other drugs?

In fact, it was Nyar Nam who made the first exit from the venue and retreated into her hut, and she did this in order to save her first cowife from additional *"wichkuot"* (shame and embarrassment) on that day.

As she prepared her sleeping mat to lie on, if one was present in the hut, they could hear her murmur these words about her first cowife, *"Njauruok ne no, ema osina."* (Her loose morals, lack of discipline and decorum, is what I hate).

The turn of events in her homestead were not only shocking by all accounts, but also historic in nature, and as she put herself to sleep, she thanked God that all this time, Nyamgondho, her husband, had not yet shown up, and this was because of obvious reasons.

However, as fate would have it, it was not long before she laid her head to rest, than she heard a loud and uniquely frightening or shreaking *"nduru"* (scream) emanating from the area further away from her hut as well as her first wife's hut, but near the gate of her *"dala!"* (homestead!)

Chapter 19

*T*he excessively loud and alarming *"nduru"* (scream) continued again and again in a way that no one in that homestead could ignore. She was half asleep as she was making it out of her door to the large *"laro"* (front yard) in the homestead which was apparently the current venue of this episode of domestic violence as she would discover in the next few moments.

As she stood in front of her hut and struggling to grip the *"ludh arungu"* (club-headed walking stick) to aid her stability in walking, she couldn't believe her ears when she heard the anger-filled conversation between her co-wife who had previously secretly slipped out of the homestead with her first co-wife, and conspired to bewitch her with the main aim of attracting her death in a manner that was not only secret, but also seemingly left no trace of crime especially to the untrained and inexperienced eyes of they who were relatively young in the so-called "game of life".

It was obvious that Nyamgondho was equally angry too. From the loud back-and-forth between the two of them, it was apparent that when Nyamgondho returned back home from his drinking spree, he found the *"rangach"* (gate) of his compound not that wide open, but was clearly evident to any *"jakal ndara"* (passers-by) or even a *"jakuo"* (thief) or *"jamaundu"* (armed robber), that the gate was not locked or secured at all.

While in as much as this was the genesis of this argument that had now escalated to a violent one, the escalation was fueled by the annoying and disrespectful words of her co-wife to her husband, especially after knowing that it was her mistake for not ensuring that the gate was not locked or secured properly before she made it to her house, as she was the last one to enter into the *"dala"* (homestead) that night before Nyamgondho.

The irate Nyamgondho continued, *"Bende ing'eyo thoth mar mwandu manitiere e dala ni mane inyalo kwal nikech gima itimoni?"* (Do you know the amount of wealth in this home that could have been stolen or robbed of us because of your negligence on this matter?). He added in a very infuriated tone, *"Koso iparo ni mwandu yot yudo nikech ichiemo nono kae?"*

(Or do you think that wealth is easy to come by because you eat free in this home?).

Before he could continue any further, Nyar Nam's co-wife in question rudely interjected into the conversation and angrily responded to Nyamgondho at the top of her voice shouting at him, "*Weya mos! Jamer mofuo ka guokni!*" (Leave me alone! A drunkard who is as foolish as a dog!).

It was as if she was sprinting with her words and she quickly added, "*In ng'ama ofuo ka odanga ma iwuondo awuonda ka apuoyoni. En ang'o ma inyalo nyisa kae?*" (You are as foolish as an elephant who is conned by a hare. What can you tell me here?).

It was at this point that Nyar Nam thought about the actions and responses of her co-wife to Nyamgondho and said in her mind, "*Yawa dhakoni kara wiye rach a racha kamae!*" (This woman is really crazy!). She continued, "*Wiye Tek mana ka ochunglo mane okayo pier Sigorma!*" (She is as tough-headed as the ant that bit the buttocks of Sigorma!)

Now, amongst the Luo people, there was famed one-of-a-kind "*Ruoth*" (Chief) named Sigorma, and Sigorma was not only famed for his charismatic, ideologue, autocratic or dictatorial leadership, but was also famed for his fierceness, aggressiveness and unwavering determination in the Luo community, and the proper or wise application of *"chike"* (laws) for the benefit or welfare of all his subjects and neighbors alike.

Chief Sigorma's towering figure as well as his *"chia maber"* (good looks), or strikingly handsome features, aided him to not only be noticed and remembered even amongst fellow chiefs, but also enabled him to be the almost-daily in-talk of the *"gwenge"* (villages) around.

In fact, it is said that, *"Onge ndalo mane kalo kata achiel ka nying Sigorma pok owachi e mieche madongo gi matindo duto"* (There was no day that passed without Sigorma's name being mentioned in both large as well as small homesteads).

Another reason as to why he was famous amongst his people is that, Sigorma was a strict disciplinarian *"mane chwado ji gi boka rao"* (who would whip those who violated or contravened the laws of the land with the famous and the feared whip made out of the skin or hides of a hippopotamus). He was also a known *"midhiero"* (mystic) who was believed to cast deadly spells on people who brushed him the wrong way.

To those who knew him in person, they could attest that Chief Sigorma "*ne en ajuoga kabisa*" (was a real wizard), "*mane ok tal*" (who was never opposed) "*to ka itale kata ichwanye, kata ugwenyre e weche mag kisera*" (and if one opposed him or argued with him, or took a different stance or point of view on matters of intimate relationships), "*to ka ok itang', to piny ok ne nyal runi ka pod ingima,* (If you were not careful, the night would not be over before that person would encounter death through mysterious spiritual means, and be pronounced dead in the following morning) .

Chief Magak "*ne en jatelo manigi mbi kabisa.*" (was a charismatic leader with a natural in-built authoritative presence).

The interesting thing is that one day while chairing a "*bura*" meeting, all over sudden, he stood up from his "*komb telo mane nigi tiendege adek*" (leadership 3-legged stool), and openly scratched his buttocks on his left side. and almost simultaneously murmuring the "Ouch!" word several times with a distorted facial expression signaling the "*lit kata rem mane owinjo*" (pain that he was experiencing.)

"*E lak seche nogono*" (In the heat of that moment), everyone looked at where he was looking at, and right on his chair was a big *"ochunglo marateng'"* (black ant) that was the culprit. The ant was *"rateng' tititi"* (completely black) *"kendo ne okaye malit kabisa"* (and bit him very painfully).

While the fellow *"jodong bura"* (elders in the meeting) were stimulated to respond in a burst of laughter to this occurrence unfolding right in front of their very own eyes especially when Chief Sigorma exclaimed that, *"Ochunglono okaya malit kabisa!"*, they dared not to do so, due to the fear of the misfortune or *"masira"* (calamity) that might befall them even including death.

"Ochunglono ne okayo pier Sigorma malit ahinya mane kanyo ne okuot ndalo adek kendo orame dweche." (That ant bit Chief Sigorma very painfully, and the actual place was swollen for three days, and was painful for a span of months). *"Lakini ne ochango maber."* (However, he recovered fully).

In sympathy to Chief Sigorma's *"rem"* (pain), one of the elders in the meeting was noted or later reported as saying, *"Yawa ochunglono wang'e Tek kabisa!"* (Wow! That ant has shameless eyes, is very tough-headed and rude!).

And so, it was at this juncture in the history of the Luo culture, that the phrase, *"Wang' matek ka ochunglo mane okayo pier Sigorma"* (Shameless eyes like those of the ant that bit the behind of Chief Sigorma), came to life amongst the people up to today.

It was almost as soon as Nyar Nam's co-wife hurled these insults to her husband that he so Nyamgondho inching much closer to her and seriously looking at her face even though "*ne omer*" (he was tipsy). She heard Nyamgondho saying out a loud, "*Yawa! Bang' ndalogi duto kara dhakoni ochayaga achaya kamae?*" (Wow! So after all this time, this woman still disrespects me to this level?).

She continued to look at him "*tir*" (straight in the eye) and it was as if she was preparing to continue with her verbal abuse, but as soon as she opened her mouth to speak, "*Nyamgondho ne omilo wang'e apat ma embe ne omuoch ka mil polo.*" (Nyamgondho slapped her thoroughly, a slap that almost sounded like lightening).

The thorough "*apat*" (slap) sent her body flying to one side, subsequently knocking her body off balance and hitting the ground with a huge thud, and what a huge thud it was. It is true that, "*dhakono ne ogoyore piny malit kabisa*" (that woman fell on the ground very painfully).

Immediately she fell down, Nyar Nam's strong and authoritative voice pierced the air with a cry for mercy from

Nyamgondho saying out aloud, "*Yaye! Weye! Oserumo! Ng'uonne!*" (Hey! Leave her alone! It is over! Forgive her!).

In as much as he did not look at her direction while she was talking, Nyamgondho looked straight at his disrespectful wife lying on the ground and made it clear to her, "*De bedni ok amer, to de atieki kabisa.*" (Had it not been that I was drunk, I would have finished you completely).

He added, "*De ing'eyo kawuono ni nyinga moro machielo en Matieka*" (You would have known today, that my other name is known as the Finisher.). And he finished by reiterating the same claim saying, "*Eh! Nyamgondho Matieka*".

While it was clear that the strength of his body was already drenched almost completely and he could barely stand upright, Nyamgondho focused his gaze to his sleeping place where he was ready to retire for the night.

The strength of his eyes were already tested by the excessive alcohol consumption as well as the length of the night that he had spent staying up and awake. However, the benevolence of the moon providing its light in the present time, aided his sight enough for him to make it to the hut that he shared with Nyar Nam, his "*Mikayi*" (first wife).

Nyar Nam watched him keenly approaching her hut and was glad that he had heeded her advice today in the heat of the moment. Having been with him for a long time, it was obvious to her that despite the fact that he was functioning relatively normally in front of other people, he was still drunk as he was a functioning alcoholic.

As he approached the door of his hut, his drunk wobbling became more pronounced and as he finally made it to the door, he was about to fall down but quickly managed to use the frame of the door to support his weight as he entered the hut. He could sense that Nyar Nam was looking at him, and so he turned around and looked at her too as was natural in the manner of response to stimuli.

It was Nyar Nam who started the conversation that would later on rank amongst the most important conversations in this narrative. She waited for Nyamgondho's eyes to lock with her eyes in this conversation and that was when out of sincere *"hera"* (love), care and concern, she asked him, *"Yawa! En ang'o machandi?"* (Oh my goodness! What is it that is bothering you?).

Upon hearing these words and acting as if he was internalizing the question and preparing to give her an honest answer. He took the opportunity to show her another side of him that he believed that "*pokne oneno nyaka nene*" (she has never seen before).

Nyamgondho looked at Nyar Nam straight in the eye and while making a fist on his right arm, he said out in a "*duol mang'ongo*" (loud voice) for all who can hear to hear these words, "*Ni kata mana ong'er moro manyocha akwanyo e kor pi ni, bende koro ochung' koda ka mieno koda weche!*". (Even a monkey that I just rescued the other day from the waters, is now standing in front of me and verbosing!).

Chapter 20

*A*lmost immediately and somehow in unisone, Nyar Nam could hear gales and gales of laughter emanating from her cowives who heard Nyamgondho utter these painful words. As soon as he had made this comment, he went straight to his bed and fell asleep as in the way of *"jokong'o"* (alcoholics or drunkards).

There was no doubt at all that he had actually meant to hurt her feelings and moroso, *"e wang' lela"* (in the public's eye), and in as much as his pride and ego could take him.

Nyar Nam stood still for a moment and in as much as *"ne inyiere"* (she was being laughed at) or even moked, her focus or attention was on the resolving of this quarrel or dispute in the home and attracting the much-needed *"kwe"* (peace) and an environment of tranquility in the ungodly hours of the night.

If she did not do so, then it was very much possible to have another heated conversation with quarelling neighbors who could claim that their night was being disturbed or their peace being upset due to the *"dhao e dalane"* (commotions in her homestead).

So she swallowed her pride and did not talk back to Nyamgondho or even respond to the insulting behavior and jeer of her cowives even though she could have successfully retaliated in order to be even with them.

If there was one thing that Nyar Nam could be remembered for, it was her herculian efforts to promote peace and attract or inspire the existence of tranquil envornments in the *"gweng'"* (village) however daunting the task would be, or however ugly the challenge would appear to present itself.

She decided to not enter her *"ot"* (house) for a moment so as to let Nyamgondho fall asleep without any other back-and-forth due to his drunkedness and an evident characteristic trait of being quick to anger. Even her fellow *"joywa rech"* (fishermen) were often heard talking about his sudden bursts of anger especially when he had gotten drunk with them.

Some were heard saying, *"Nyamgondho en jamirima kabisa"* (Nyamgondho is a person who is quick to anger), while yet others were often heard saying, "*Mirimb Nyamgondho kata ich wang' mare, en gima nyalo chwer ka koth machwer mang'eny e diemo wang!*" (Nyamgondho's wrath or his bursts of anger, can at times be compared to rain that rains heavily and in an instant!).

Despite the small crowd of her cowives that had gathered around her hut to witness if she was going to get beaten, or if she herself was going to revenge on Nyamgondho for his unkind or "choice" words unto her and especially in public, Nyar Nam decided to sit quietly in the "*ndiri*" (raised seating area all around her hut) for some quiet time of self discovery or self mastery or, even the feasting on the wise or profound teachings and words of wisdom that she had never thought of in the same fashion.

It was with heavy feet that her cowives finally left to return to their respective huts and more so, their respective beds or sleeping mats in order to catch some sleep again, before the time to "*chieo*" (waking up) reached. Before long, she found herself the only one remaining in the outside of a house or hut and probably the only one awake in the homestead at that time.

As she sat all by herself there out of neccessity of "kwe" (peace), tears welled in her eyes at the behaviour, manner of life and the vexing or anger-inspiring speech of Nyamgondho to her and especially *"e wang lela"* (in the nakedness of the public), and at this ungodly hour.

In such circumstances, it was Nyar Nam's method of reasoning that forced her to ponder on the actual root or the root causes of these unique outbursts of violent-filled phenomenon in an otherwise peaceful environment.

It was at these times that the words, teachings or even the counsel of the man of authority of whom she always quoted in her teachings, would spring back up from another part of her memory to the frontline of her thoughts.

While in a pensive mood, she thought about the legitimate questions or challenges that were possible to be entertained in the minds of Nyamgondho and her irrate and jealous, cowives and often found out that in as much as they sought pragmatic or practical solutions for themselves in their lives, some or even a few of them, accepted or internalized the harsh reality that every problem is a solution, and every solution is a problem too!

In other words, in the course of going through my life or sailing, or navigating the seemingly turbulent wates of mortaility in this probationary period of life on this sanguine planet, it is wise to appreciate the profound fact that, the solutions that I have attracted to my life, or the answers that I am seeking in my life or the lives of my loved ones, are simoultaneously also problems or even serious challenges to other people, and vice versa.

If one would reason or follow this rightful logic, they would come to a point in their reasoning as to conclude that in as much as one who is sincerely diligent in their search for knowledge, truth and understanding can finally know all their is to know as well as understand all that there is to understand; If they be more diligent and more objective rather than being subjective in their search, they will also find out that, all that there is to be known and understood, is not the entire spectrum of existence!

Oh yes! And Nyar Nam knew this even from the very first principles of thought itself and that, there is that which is in existence but defies definition, and hence is categorized or classified as the undefined. And it was actually from the undefined, that the defined comes from, and the undefined has no opposites as this was, is, and shall continue to be at the bedrock of the undefined.

Yet another way to look at definition, is that in all that is defined by man, man was only able to define it conclusively by focusing on the opposite of it e.g. the definition of light is conclusive because one has an idea of darkness, the definition of bitter is only conclusive because one has the idea of sweet or has experienced sweetness. The same is true for happiness and sadness, smiles and frowns as well as many other examples.

And so, if one day in the rigours or journey of one's life, they happen to meet or come accross a one-of-a-kind phenomenon or occurence that is unique and has no opposites like going to fish for real fish, but finding a human being trapped in the fish traps for example, wouldn't this *"midhiero"* (mystery) alone, inspire one to fear or respect the person especially if such a person is the source of the *"wealth"* (jewels or treasures) in their life?

Nyar Nam's thoughts went real deep on this one as the *"mirima"* (anger) that Nyamgondho's words evoked in her mind, was more than she had ever felt in her entire life with him since they met.

Even if Nyamgondho wanted to know all that there is to know and even understand all that there is to understand about her but had been defeated or failed to do so, he should have remembered the wise counsel of the man of authority that Nyar Nam taught her earlier on in their relationship which taught that, "The wind bloweth where it listeth, and though hearest the sound thereof, but canst not tell whence it cometh, and whither it goeth: so is everyone that is born of the Spirit."

She remembered this occasion very well that in as much as Nyamgondho was receptive to this kind of teaching, knowledge and understanding, the vocabularly that was used in imparting such wise counsel was very deep and sometimes sounded awkward to one who was no accustomed or acclimatized to such language or expressions.

In fact, to further expound on this wise counsel, Nyar Nam remembered even telling Nyamgondho that the Spirit is also referred to as "*yamo*" (wind), and even "*muya*" (breath) and yet in another language called Greek, the spirit, wind and breath were all referred to as *pneuma*.

She even proceeded to state this wise counsel in simple terms for easier understanding and telling him that, "The wind blows where it whishes, and you hear its sound, but you do not know where it comes from or where it goes. So it is with everyone who is born of the Spirit."

Nyar Nam still remembers very vividly that during this specific lesson, Nyamgondho was very concerned that even if he started to tread along the paths of rightousness as per the standards of such teachings, he knew that he would not succeed that much as he recognized his weaknesses as a man, and was reluctant to change them due to the Herculian effort that was needed to be employeed in acquiring such a coveted status.

In as much as Nyar Nam acknowledged his sincere concerns and appreciated his honesty in his response, she still encouraged her by saying that there was nothing wrong for a baby to take baby steps in the right direction, and learning how to walk without falling and sometimes injuring oneself, is often unheard of!

The overriding theme or focus of relevance here, was to think of the joy of walking or even being able to walk correctly, and even now being able to sprint or run; And, then stop for a moment and think, or even ponder on whether it was worth picking up one-self after falling while trying to learn how to walk, even if it meant dealing with tears here and there due to injuries sustained while in the progress of learning, mastering or even horning the skill-set of "*wuotho*" (walking) especially when moral values as well as standards of integrity, or even ethics in our dealings with our fellow man, was in question.

Apart from reminding him to think about the joy of the accomplishment or success of overcoming obstruction and mastering a much-needed skill-set of survival in nature, she also reminded him of another episode of the counsel shared with her from the man of authority who also quoted the sincere and genuine experience of how in as much as he managed to live a righteous life, he could not help to ignore the facts or challenges of dealing with the thoughts of backsliding or regressing in his unwavering commitment to live by the laws or guidelines of righteous living.

And in his true testimony, he shared these words or sentiments, "I do not understand what I do. For what I want to do I do not do, but what I hate I do. And if I do what I do not want to do, I agree that the law is good. And it is, it is no longer I myself who do it, but it is sin living in me. For I know that good itself does not dwell in me, that is, in my sinful nature. For I have the desire to do what is good, but I cannot carry it out. For I do not do the good I want to do, but the evil I do not want to do - this I keep on doing. Now if I do what I do not want to do, it is no longer I who do it, but it is sin living in me that does it. So I find this law at work: Although I want to do good, evil is right there with me."

As he marvelled on such truths and pondered on them, Nyar Nam added yet another set of wise counsel taught by the man of authority that said, "The race is not to the swift, nor the battle to the strong, neither yet bread to the wise, nor yet riches to men of understanding, not yet favor to men of skill; but time and chance happeneth to them all."

It was obvious that quite a bit of time had passed since she began to sit in the "*ndiri*" outside the front door of her hut, and by looking at the moon and the signature of the stars in their various constellations in the sky, she knew that the wee hours of the morning were fast approaching and she sincerely needed to catch some "*nindo*" (sleep) if she was to function well physically the next day.

But before she left her seating position for her bed in her hut, she took a very keen look at her "*ludh arungu*" (club-headed walking stick), and while gripping it very tight with her right hand, she stood up and while still holding it, she went into a pensive mood but finally, she uttered these words under her breath, *"Ludhani ema adhi tiyogodo"* (This walking stick of mine, is what I am going to use).

It was very clear, that Nyar Nam had just devised a plan of action for her *"chulo kuor"* (revenge), and was now racing against time to execute it. With a sigh of great relief, she continued, *"Eh! To ludhani, ne par gi ogendni duto te e piny kae higni gi higni!"* (Oh Yes! And, this walking stick of mine, will be remembered by all generations of people on this earth year in, year out!).

Chapter 21

With a lot of pain in her physical body as well as *"lit e chunye"* (anguish in her soul), it was obvious that she struggled to stand up from her seating position outside her hut as she headed slowly and quietly into her hut to catch some sleep. She made sure that she tip-toed to her bed as she did not want to interrupt her husband's sleep or comfort in her house.

She managed to stretch herself on the bed after *"yiengo ludhe e kor ot"* (leaning her walking stick on the wall) and withn no time, she was first asleep despite the relatively loud *"twaro"* (snoring) of Nyamgondho.

In as much as her mind was still in deep thought and she could have philosophized even more in her thought structures or patterns of thinking, she opted to switch off her brain in order to rest her body as it was also a healthy choice to do so.

After finally getting some *"nindo"* (sleep), it so happened that in as much as she heard the first crow of the cork in the homestead, this time round, she was not the first one to rise up or wake up from the bed, and it was definitely not because of *"nyao"* (laziness) or *"ywaruok"* (sluggishness) as was often the case with many people especially women who absconded from their duties in the homestead, and were commonly referred to as *"mon maywayore"* (sluggish women).

It was a few minutes past *"saa adek ma okinyi"* (nine o'clock in the morning) when Nyar Nam's eyes opened again to the world. Oh yes! She was now fully awake even though *"dende pod ne ool kendo rame bende."* (her body was still tired and sore).

The most important thing for her to remember right now, was that she had already set up her mind on what to do today in her homestead, and it was going to be a historic event such as has never been seen or heard of in the entire Luoland, and even *"e mieche mag mweche ma ong'e kanyo"* (in the villages of members of neighboring tribes known to them).

As she looked to the other side of the bed, she noticed that Nyamgondho was still deep asleep and snoring as usual without any thought at all that being a *"Jaduong' mar dala"*

(The head of the homestead). he should have been amongst the first to wake up and inspire his *"langi"* (family), to chase as well as treasure the noble values of life of which hard work, strong work ethic, diligence, patience, edurance, discipline and determination, and even self-determination, were to be cherished and upheld at all times in the life of any man or woman, young or old.

She first sat on the bed for a few moments with her arms resting on the bed but backwards of her body. All this time, Nyamgondho, her husband, did not even appear to be awake or could be woke up to respond to urgent matters.

She quickly glanced at her *"kendo"* (fireplace) but this time round, she did not look at it with the intention of making a fire to at least warm up some *"nyuka"* (porridge) or prepare some breakfast, but she looked at it for another reason.

Next, she looked at the *"aguch pi"* (water pot) in the house and immediatey knew that in as much as she was going to skip breakfast, her body needed the ample or enough amounts of water for obvious reasons as well as for other reasons that were not so obvious but was going to be apparent as the day unfolded itself or as the *"chieng'"* (sun) continued to soar up in the sky from the its resting place in the horizons.

She quickly got out of her bed and walked to the water pot, and helped herself to some drinking water using the *"aguata mang'ongo"* (large calabash) available there. She then opened her door for the *"yamo maler"* (fresh air) as well as sunshine to bless the house with their healing effects as was normal when one experienced basking in the sun on a warm summer day without excessive humidity.

No sooner had she opened her door, that she so several of her cowive's doors also opening, but this time round, almost all of them were straring at her with expectant eyes, while others were outrightly mocking her, and laughing in low tones.

She could hear one saying to another, *"Manyale."*(Sweet revenge), and she continued by saying out aloud that, *"Makata Nyamgondho a dik wiye matek kaka lwanda, kata go wiye gi arungu."* (How I wish that Nyamgondho would have hit her head like a rock, or clobbered her head with a club).

It was right after this occurence or episode, that Nyar Nam seized the moment to reach into her hut and grab her *"ludh arungu"* (club-like walking stick) and off she eased herself outside her hut, walked cautiously and finally stepped into the middle of the homestead.

It was while here that she stood still in *"e chuny dala"* (the middle of the homestead) and shouted out *"matek"* (aloud), an immediate *"chik"* (command) that would almost immediately define the new and unexpected course of history of all of that homestead including its chatel as well as all that could be defined or categorized as *"mwandu mar adieri"* (real wealth) to any man in that day and time.

In a loud, steady and firm voice, Nyar Nam proceeded to orate the command saying, *"Mwanduna duto! Lua uru..."* (All my wealth! Follow me...).

It was at this point that all who were present were not only shocked at what they were seeing, but were terrified at the immense *"tekre mag roho"* (spiritual power) that Nyar Nam not only possessed, but also commanded and knew how to use, direct or channel in the directions of her choice, and for her own gratification as well as defense.

From the *"dhok"* (cattled) in the *"kul"* (animal shed), all the way to the smallest *"gweno"* (chicken), left their cocoons or places of domiscile. and started moving to the front of her *"laro"* (frontyard of the homestead).

It was when the first couple of cows actually came and stood infront of her like soldiers lining up in pairs infront of their commander, that one of her cowives shouted out aloud for all those who were not in the vicinity, to come and witness this one-of-a-kind and never-seen-before "*midhiero*" (mysterious spectacle of occurence).

As she continued to gaze at this seemingly impossible occurence or happening, she shouted out aloud on top of her lungs saying, "*Mayie! Bi uneye kaka Nyar Nam wuoyo go dhok kod chiae kod gwen duto!*" (Oh my God! Come and see how Nyar Nam is talking to cattle, sheep, goats and even all the chicken!).

She continued, "*Ma en midhiero manade? Aneno wang'a koso bin pod aleko?*" (What kind of mistery is this? I'm I hallucinating or still dreaming?).

When she finished saying, "*Aneno wang'a koso bin pod aleko*" (I'm I hallucinating or still dreaming?), she quickly and almost without thinking, touched both of her eyes and rubbed them thoroughly to ensure that she was perfectly awake and normal in the head.

As she was doing this, a sizeable crowd from the homestead had already gathered to witness this misterious and one-of-a-kind scene, however, her shouting out aloud, had also attracted the attention of *"jirende"* (neighbors) as well as *"jokadh ndara"* (passers-by) who were equally stunned at what they were seeing.

Nyar Nam stood still as she watch all her livestock gather in an organized fashion right infront of her like school children in a morning assembly or soldiers parading themselves in a disciplined army ready to receive a new, timely and important set of instructions.

It was interesting as to how all the three gates of the *"kul"* (cattle sheds) that contained all the cattle in the *"dala"* (homestead), opened up themselves to let the cattle free without the help of anyone.

In those days and times, it was normal and customary for the *"rombe"* (sheep), *"diel"* (goats) and *"gwen"* (chicken), to be housed in a real mud-thatched house like houses built for human living not only due to the harsh or servere weather conditions that could kill them or introduce sickness unto them, but also to protect them from the marauding and notorious *"ondiegi"* (hyenas) and *"kwach"* (leopard) that occasionally strayed from the nearby *"thim"* (wilderness) and preyed on them causing very painful and massive losses to the owners of such *"chiae"* (livestock).

On this very day, also all the mud-thatches huts that housed all the *"rombe"* (sheep), goats and chicken in the homestead, despite being locked securely, opened themsleves and let all the domesticated animals out.

As the chicken were also lining up in the front yard of the homestead, one of Nyar Nam's cowife, ran to the hut that housed the chicken to see if all the chicken had left including those that were recently hatched and were caged in the *"asere"* (mobile chicken coupe) that protected them from the fiery eyes of predators like *"otenga"* (eagles) and the strong *"tielo"* (feet) of a multitude of larger chicken in the hut.

And it was to her utter dismay that even the *"gwen matindo"* (small chicken) had gathered new and inexplicable strength from nowhere and got out of their mobile chicken coupes, and were headed for the mysterious assembly infront of Nyar Nam in the *"laro"* (frontyard of the homestead)! Oh yes! As she looked inside the chicken house, she so that all the *"asere"* (mobile chicken coupe), *"ne olokore ataro kendo ne odong' nono"* (were turned upside down and were empty).

Apart from being a "*Dhako ma jawuoro*" (gluttonious woman), "*kod ngudi*" (and mean-spirited selfish person), one of the main reasons as to why she was focused on checking out the chicken house, was because amongst her favorite dishes was "*kuon*" (maize meal) kod "*gweno*" (chicken), and being married into a family of wealth untold, one of her secret incentives to live in this "*dala*" (homestead) was the ability to eat as much chicken as she wanted as there was more than plenty to "*chinjo*" (slaughter) and "*chamo*" (delight in or eat) even if it was an everyday occurence.

As it it was true that this cowife "*ne en dhako ma ohero hetho kabisa*" (was a woman who enjoyed to eat in a hurried fashion), "*kod ketho chiemo*" (and wasting of food), "*kaachiel kod nyao*" (as well as laziness), this was a real and total blow to her survival in this homestead, and as the reality of this almost-instantenous and unfortunate circumstance began to sink into her mind, her "*tielo*" (legs) suddenly became week and she fell by the doorside of the chicken house with tears rolling down her cheeks.

"*Eh! Ywak ne nitiere kendo malit kabisa.*" (Oh yes! There was a lot of weeping, and very painful weeping it was). It was then that she exclaimed, "*Yawa! Wang'ni to gwen te orumo!*" (Wow! This time round, all the chicken are gone!"

"*Yawa! Otimore nade? Tinde wachak nade?*" (Wow! How has this happened? Where should I start in responding to this calamity?) She asked herself a series of rhetorical questions one after another.

It was also true that women of this nature were not marketable at all in "*kend*" (marriage), as they were known as to be "*nyiri mokethore*" (spoilt women) and "*mon mathembo athemba e mieche ji.*" (Women who were just travelling into people's homes without the desire to stick into a responsible and respectable relationship).

They were also known to "*Lombo ji kod mbaka mag oyuma, ma thuo ji kendo ketho ute ji machiegni kod maboyo.*" (Seducing people with "sweet nothings" and gossips that inspire internal feuds or domestic rows, or violence that ultimately destroys the homes as well as long-term relationships of other people both near and distant).

Had it not been for Nyamgondho's "*chode kod kong'o*" (loose morals and alcoholism), she would never have put her "*tielo*" (foot) on this homestead or even found a "*dala kae*" (an abode here).

There was no doubt that this was a heavy blow for her and the maintenance of her egoistic lifestlye of *"sunga"* (pride) and *"nyietho"* (showing off) to her fellow *"mon"* (women) and *"mbese e gweng'"* (agemates alike in the village).

As if that was not enough, all the specators here today, marvelled the more on this mysterious occurence as even the several *"dero mopogore opogore"* (granaries of all kinds) present in the homestead, also came and joined the *"jamni"* (all the livestock) in their parading or assembly infront of Nyar Nam. This was really strange but it was happining here today in this part of Luoland!

Unlike many homesteads that were not as blessed with wealth and spleandor, it was normal for homes that were full of fortune like Nyamgondho's to have several granaries or huts that housed different kinds of *"chiemo"* (foodstuffs) as well as some specifically built or erected to house the *"kodhi"* (seeds) of grains to be planted in the successive seasons to come.

Yet still, some *"dero"* (granaries) were erected specifically to house *"aliya"* (dried, cured or specially treated meats to last longer without decaying). Such forms of preservatives or treatments were also used even for some kinds of *"rech"* (fish), and if done well enough, such fish could last in the storage for even a *"higa"* (year) or so. Such fish were known as *"obambla"* (dried fish) or commonly referred to by many using the slang language as *"obambo"*.

When all these forms or types of *"mwandu"* (wealth) had completed assembling in front of Nyar Nam, it was then that she uttered another *"chik"* (command) or instruction unto them that was short yet uniquely powerful.

With the loud shouting, exclammations, noise from the *"jamni"* (domesticated animals), and strange happenings, quite a sizeable crowd had gathered both *"ei dala"* (in the compound) as well as around the fence of it, and the front of the *"rangach"* (gate) with their curious *"wenge"* (eyes) struggling not to even blink *"kata nyadichiel"* (once or for a moment).

Even though all her wealth had gathered together in front of her and was waiting for the next instruction from her, there was a noticeable moment of silence that could not escape the attention of all that were following this series of events unfolding or unravelling right in front of their very own eyes and in broad daylight.

As they stood watching Nyar Nam, they noticed that she was seriously focusing her gaze on the front of her *"ot"* (house) in the *"dala"* (homestead) as if she was expecting something important to happen there.

And as the crowd continued to help her in directing their views to the front of her house, for a moment, they wondered why despite all these happenings and noise in the homestead, Nyamgondho, her husband and the head of the homestead, was nowhere to be seen! Had he died or what?

Chapter 22

*H*aving known Nyar Nam as a *"dhako ma ratiro"* (an upright woman), kendo *"dhako ma odimbore"* (a woman of impeccable manners and an observant of protocol), it was then that one of her cowives quickly read *"in-between-the-lines"* and realized that Nyar Nam was seeking a public audience with her husband, and due to her nature, she was not going to interrupt his sleep, but was going to wait until Nyamgondho, her husband, wakes up from his drunken sleep before she makes her next move.

Also, having known Nyamgondho well enough, this cowife aslo knew or predicted that given the fact that Nyamgondho was excessively drunk last night, it was going to be way past noon before he actually woke up today as this had gradually become his well-known nature in such occasions.

The time right now was not even *"saa ang'wen mar okinyi"* (ten o'clock in the morning) and she could not stand the waiting time for some action. She knew that she had to do something to attract Nyamgondho's attention on this matter, and whatever she had to do, she had to do it quickly.

Being that this was also her home and she basically needed no permission to go into anywhere where her husband was or to inquire of his well-being or wherereabouts, she quickly strode into Nyar Nam's hut in a quest to bring Nyamgondho's attention to the unexpected happenings in the homestead that required his immediate attention as "wuon dala" (head of the homestead).

As soon as she entered the hut, she could see that Nyamgondho had "*layo*" (urinated) on himself and was still asleep and was snoring away the morning.

Given the circumstances of her visit and the urgency of the matter at hand, she did not fear being beaten or being cursed out for suddenly waking him up, as the wrath of his anger was now a secondary priority to her.

After calling his name out several times and nudging him on the shoulders but only receiving groanings for a response, "*iye ne owang*" (she got upset) and got a different idea of attracting his immediate attention or "*chiewe*" (waking him up).

She dashed to the "*dapi*" (drinking water pot) and grabbed the calabash in her hand, and used it to grab some water from the pot, and poured the cold water on him with seething anger stirring in her guts as to how a "*Jaduong' dala ma rahuma kamae*" (The head of a Household of this repute) can afford to "*nindo e lak sechegei*" (sleep at this time), with all the strange happenings in his homestead.

Immediately, Nyamgondho woke up and sat on the bed. As he shook his head and attempted to wipe the urine off his skin, it was evident that he was very annoyed yet puzzled.

He knew that he was in Nyar Nam's hut but what was his other wife doing here when Nyar Nam was not present? As he looked at her face in demand for immediate answers, she also likewise looked at her face in search for action as to what was going on "*oko kacha*" (outside there).

She stood right in front of him and pointing at the door with her right hand while painting a sense of urgency with her facial expressions. Nyamgondho was now wide awake and very alert and knew that he was not in a dream or experiencing some fantasy, but something out of the ordinary was happening in his homestead that needed his immediate action.

The closest weapon that he could grab was his "*tong*" (spear) and he stood up in a hurried fashion. He also put on his back his "*asere*" (bow and quiver of arrows), and in almost the wink of an eye, he was out of the hut that he shared with Nyar Nam.

Now, just like all who were here and spectating and following the turn of events in this homestead today, Nyamgondho was not an exception to the "*bwok*" (shock) that met his eyes.

It was clear that whatever was happening here and with the assembly of all his "*mwandu*" (wealth) in the "*laro*" (frontyard) did not happen in the wink of an eye. An intense feeling of "*kuyo*" (sorrow) and great "*wichkuot*" (shame and embarrassment) engulfed him like a blanket wraps itself around an infant ir a baby.

But how come that he had not heard even the slightest mowing of the "*dhok*" (cows) or the bleeting of the "*rombe*" (sheep) or "*diek*" (goats), or even at least a cluck of the numerous and almost uncountable "gwen" (chicken) that were right in front of her hut?

How could this have been happening without his attention or even without his permission as "*wuon dala*" (owner of the home)?

As he took a quick glance at Nyar Nam, quite close to her were "*choice bread*" amongst the "*rwedhe*" (bulls) that Nyamgondho prided himself with, and it was now clear unto him that Nyar Nam was planning to exit the home with them.

The pain of loosing such wealth suddenly became very apparent to him and the more he thought about it, the more "*ne lit ne kabisa*" (he couldn't bear it).

Suddenly, he dashed back into the hut and dropped his weapons as he did not need them in this matter, but instead, he quickly got himself a very strong "*ludh kwath*" (Shepherd's rod) of which he planned on shepherding or driving back all his livestock to their respective sheds or places of domiscile, as they sort out this matter with Nyar Nam later on. He had to do something not only to secure his wealth back, but to also cover his shame.

He stepped out of Nyar Nam's hut and headed straight to her in a mood for dialogue but to his utter dismay, upon seeing him coming closer, Nyar Nam gave a very simple but firm instruction to all her "*mwandu*" in this homestead; And, in this instruction, she said unto them, "*Mwanduga duto tetete, Luwa uru.*" (All my wealth, follow me).

As soon as she uttered these words unto them, she turned her head towards the gate of the "*dala*" (homestead) to signal all who were standing there to give way, and subsequently, she also turned her body towards the "*rangach*" (gate) and led the famous "*wuoth*" (walk) back to the "*Nam*" (Lake) where she came from.

Chief Leinad Ongoda was really suprised at the memory that Rieko posessed as well as his ability to recall "*weche*" (words) and phrases from his grandfather's Luo ancestry, and articulately narrate this story even though it was quite a few summers ago when Chief Leinad Ongoda narrated this story unto the for the first time.

Chief knew that due to the limitations of ancestral stories being passed down from one generation to another through "*sigendni*" (oral narratives), there may have been some inconsistencies in the minor details of the "*sigana*" (story); However, the "*kithor mar weche*" (overriding themes), as well as the "spirit" and moral of that story, remained the same almost in all of the narrative.

In as much as this was true, there was some unique detail about this story that was only known and understood by the *"Jomidhiero"* (mystics) alone in the Luo culture that Chief Leinad Ongoda hailed from, and due to the fact that he himself was a *"Jakoro"* (Prophet mystic), he knew it.

Amongst those details was the fact that Nyamgondho first meeting with Nyar Nam was by the shores of a *"aora"* (river) and not a lake; However, this detail was not as neccessary for one to benefit from the morals of the story.

Chief Leinad Ongoda stilled his thoughts and allowed himself to continue listening to the last parts of this narrative as was being narrated by Rieko, his great grandson of whom he was pleased. And so he continued to listen to him like all the rest in attendance of this one-of-a-kind occasion.

In as much as almost all members of the homestead as well as the villagers coveted or salivated on this massive wealth, none of them could get a hold of it or even grab the most succeptible part of it to be grabbed, easily gotten away with, or stolen.

This was mainly because of the fact that as soon as Nyar Nam started her historic exodus or departure from the *"dala"* (homestead), the feet of all men and women including

Nyamgondho and the "*nyithindo*" (children) mysteriously stuck to the ground making them immobile till she left the village entirely.

It was true that, "*Kane Nyamgondho ne oneno rwedhe madongo dongo ka ringo kendo weyo dalane, ne ohum nono ma ogoyo uwi malit kabisa ka okok gi nying Nyar Nam.*" (When Nyamgondho so that his best and fattest of bulls running away and leaving his homestead, he was so shocked that he cried out aloud and wailed wildely while calling out the name of Nyar Nam).

"*Eh.*" (Oh Yes!). "*Magie duto ne otimore e kor odiechieng' e wang' lela ka ji duto tendeng' nyaka jirende kod jokal ndara neno kamae gi wengegi, ka dala Nyamgondho dong' gunda, kendo ka mwanduge duto te ochomo ndara tir kendo ringo ka weye gi lwete nono.*" (All these events happened in the broad daylight when everyone including the neighbors and passersby, witnessed with their very own eyes when Nyamgondho's home became deserted, and how his immense wealth was headed out of his home and into the road, away from him, and leaving him empty-handed).

While almost reaching the shores of the lake, one of the villagers was heard exclaiming out aloud saying that, "*Ei yawa! Kare mane waneno mana ni jamni kod gikmokogi, kara ne gin mana askeche mag Nyar Nam ma rite kende luo mana chikege tir?"* (Oh wow! So, is it true that whatever we used to see as cattle, or mere chatel and foodstuff belonging to Nyar Nam, was actually her soldiers or security detail that obeys her command, and obeys even to the letter?

It also happened that all over sudden, when Nyar Nam reached the shores of the lake, all the legs of the *"jogweng'"* (villagers) regained their mobility and could once again walk and move about.

The interesting thing is that, they who were sick or feeling unwell before they had this strange phenomenon happen to them, claimed that they were completely healed and felt a fresh new vitality and energy in them that they craved or yearned for but had never gotten!

Even Nyamgondho himself, upon gaining back the strength of his feet, was heard giving a testimony to his wives that, *"Awinjo ka kong'o tetete orumo e wiya!"* (I feel that all the alcohol in my head is gone completely!), *"Kendo kata wichbar kod jony mane an godo koro awinjo ka orumo kabisa!"* (Even the headache and the general body tiredness that I was feeling, is gone completely!). And everybody around him could suddenly see that he no longer had any signs of hangover at all.

However, he was very depressed and knew that he was indeed in deep trouble in his once-famous and well-reputed home; And, in as much as pride had created a strong foundation in his character over the years, it was not going to be possible for him to regain back his wealth and status in the community if he did not embrace the tennets of utmost humility in his next plan of action, or tact, or skill of at least saving his name in the public domain.

All of a sudden, his feet felt lighter and lighter as the option of reconciling with Nyar Nam through asking for forgiveness or being apologetic even if it meant putting up a public show, came into or bounced into his otherwise now uniquely-prideful mind filled with an uncontrolled or unchecked ego, coupled with a boistreous attitude, and unbriddled passions.

As this thought of asking for forgiveness and reconcilliation started to take center-stage in his mind, it was in the affirmative that if he did not seize the moment and act swiftly, then all would be lost and even be lost for ever and never to return.

With his "*ludh kwath*" (Shepherd's rod) still in his hands, he dashed to the gate while shouting out aloud to his remaining wifes where he was going telling them that, "*Adhi lao Nyar Nam mondo aduok mwandun!*" (I am going after Nyar Nam so as to bring back my wealth!).

As they watched him sprint out of the "*rangach*" (gate), one of the cowives was heard by a neigbor conversing in low tones with another of her fellow cowife saying, "*Yawa! Ma koro osemaye mwanduni malitni, pod oonge kata gi wichkuot mar goyone Nyar Nam mos mar adieri!*" (Wow! Now that his wealth has embarrassingly and painfully been taken away from him, he still does not have the shame that can compel him to be at least sincerely apologetic to Nyar Nam or be honestly remorseful for his evil and mean deeds!).

She continued, "*Mayie! Ma en ng'ama chal nadeni?* (Oh my God! What kind of a person is this?) With great amounts of ire or angst, or anger raging in her bossom and very much evident in her eyes, she continued, "*En mwandune kod morne kende ema nenone moloyo gimora amore e kendni ma kata wan ok odew wa?*" (Only his personal wealth and personal happiness is of utmost importance in this marriage, without even thinking of us?).

She completed her observation by saying, "*Yawa! Ma en ng'ama kite rach kendo ngudi ma pok adwaro aneno e pinynie!*" (Wow! This is the most evil-spirited and selfish person that I have ever seen or come accross in this world!).

Meanwhile, as Nyamgodho hurriedly made his way to Nyar Nam before she could disappear for ever, he sprinted as fast as his legs could carry him but it was very much evident that Nyar Nam had covered a lot of distance on her journey by this time, and the chances or odds of "*make*" (catching up) with her were growing slim.

However, he encouraged himself with the fact that if he succeeded, he was going to get his wealth and status back as well as an opportunity of "*chulo kuor kuome*" (revening on her).

Oh yes! Being the person that he had become, there was more of revenge that filled his mind rather than true or sincere apology. He said to himself about Nyar Nam, "*Adwaro hoye ahoya mondo odwogi.*" (I just want to comfort her so that she can come back).

He continued in his thoughts, "*To bang' koseduogo ma gikmoko okwe, to abiro goye goch ma nyamin anega, ma ok nochak otug koda kendo bilani.*" (And when she comes back and everything settles down, I will give her a thorough beating that she will never ever think of doing a similar thing again as this).

While on his way to the lake, Nyamgodho so many villagers that had lined up on the side of the road to watch or witness the historic and one-of-a-kind mass exodus of Nyar Nam and her "*mwandu*" to wherever she was going. Some villages also due to the fear of the occurence of "*midhieche*" (mysteries), decided to watch this phenomenon from the confines of their "*miechgi*" (homes) while craning from the top of their fences.

It was at this moment that Nyamgondho experienced that which made him be full of regrets. Amongst these fellow villagers who had witnessed his "*wichkuot mang'ongo*" (big shame and embarassment) as well as the immense loss of historic proportions of his wealth, only a handful simpathized with him, but of particular importance was the masses who laughed at him, moked him and made fun of him "*e wang' lela*" (in public) even as he embarassed Nyar Nam in earlier episodes of their interraction in their homestead.

It really pained him that amongst the characters that laughed at him, mocked him, magnified his downfall from grace, and hurled "*ayenje madongo dongo*" (big insults) at him as well as publicly embarassing him, were they who had benefited from him immensely whenever he met them at the *"ute mag bayo, kong'o, miel kod chode"* (equvalent of bars, brothels, clubs, pubs and other similar places).

While it was hard to gather the courage to go on in his reconciliatory mission of personal redemption, he consoled himself with the thought that in the event that he got back his *"mwandu"* (wealth), he will surely get a chance to revenge even more.

As he continued with his journey towards Nyar Nam, it was however sincerely true and very much evident that, *"E lak seche mane Nyamgondho onwang'e masira, osiepege duto mane obayogodo, ne oringe."* (At the time that Nyamgondho suffered this tribulation, all his drinking and merry-making friends or buddies, fled away from him).

It was like a breath of fresh air when he finally got a glimpse of his *"dhok"* (cows) or chatel already by the lakeside.

The harsh reality is that most of them had already disappeared into the lake where Nyar Nam came from, and it was as if he also so an old man leaning on a tall but elegantly sculptured *"luth"* (walking stick) on his right hand, and when he so him, *"ne okonyo Nyar Nam piko mwanduge kuma ne oaye."* (he was aiding Nyar Nam to return her wealth from where she came from). It was as if he was providing some *"ohinga"* (security) as well as overseeing Nyar Nam completing her *"wuoth"* (journey) as he stood confidently on the *"pi"* (waters) of the lake unshaken or unmoved at all!

Chapter 23

A t this point, Nyamgondho was not shaken that much on the "*midhieche*" (mysterious happenings) that he so or experienced since he woke up that morning as it was obvious that they were more than he could count, and his priority at hand was not that much to marvel at miracles or fear miracle workers or magicians, but to reclaim back his lost wealth as well as restore his already destroyed name.

He knew and understood very well that these set of occurences and unexpected painful, shameful and embarassing scenarios would have been avoided had it not have been for his already tarnished character.

It was clear in his mind that Nyar Nam had no fault at all in this "*dhao kata gwenyruok*" (feud or debacle), and in fact, if Nyar Nam was equally of a "*chulo kwor*" (revengeful) character as him, she would have easily killed him already in his deep drunken sleep as soon as he fell asleep last night.

In as much as he was not shaken that much by the miraculous happenings in his presence at this point in time, it was also true that he couldn't ignore the fact that something strange was happening between him and the old man leaning on a tall and uniquely sculptured walking stick that looked like a decorative but tough *"ludh kwath"* (shepherd's staff) and standing comfortably on the top of the waters of the lake.

As he approached the lake in a hurried manner, it was as if, that the closer he got to the venue in question, the lighter or more pale the body of the old man became, until he finally became invisible when Nyamgondho reached at a talking distance to Nyar Nam.

This was very strange indeed. How could you see a person from afar, but when you approach him, he doesn't move but he fades away as you near his presence, and disappears into the thin air!

While he was still afar and seeing him, some of his confidence of success in these reconciliatory talks with Nyar Nam, was significantly boosted as he had thought that since he had a witness to this feud, and being that the witness was a man like him, he could request for his support to convince Nyar

Nam to rethink her position on this matter, and to forgive and forget as they focus on a fresh start in their relationship.

But as the old man started to become invinsibe with every step that he took towards him, his hopes for success dwindled quite a bit, and from a sincere or truthful point of view, he did not know how to start or commence this conversation. He had now gotten relatively close to Nyar Nam and feared to move closer to her even more lest he experience another miracle that could paralize or even anihilate him completely.

Oh yes! He knew that in his long-term relationship with Nyar Nam, gradually his previously cherished and much appreciated characteristic attributes of patience, kindness and peace-loving, had gradually and steadily been replaced with noticiable envy especially of *"monde ji kata monde jomoko"* (other peoples wives) leading him to marry other wives in great haste without even taking his time to learn of their past or the nature of the families that they came from.

He began to boast openly of his newly-acquired or ammersed wealth, became uniquely arrogant, extravagant, rude as well as rejoicing in wrongdoing like *"jaro ji"* (exposing other people's shame to the public with the intention of laughing at them or hurting them), "*chayo ji*" (disrespecting other people), outright "*chode*" (loose morals), "*mer oko mar dala*" (public drunkedness), "*goch*" (physical fighting) and even "*chulo kuor*" (revenging) as he had already planned in his head to teach Nyar Nam a very painful and memorable lesson, as well as all those who laughed at him when this "*masira*" (calamity) befel him.

Interestingly enough, right in front of his eyes, just like some "*hono*" (miracle), a bunch of very beautiful and uniquely captivating growth of fresh "*maua*" (flowers) immediately sprung up from the "*lo*" (ground), and sorrounded Nyar Nam in a very phenomenal and unforgateable fashion.

In as much as this process was immediate, the flowers spread themselves around Nyar Nam in a very signature and spectacular array of colours that even Nyamgodho himself was tempted to enter into, but then, he so the sharp thorns that secured the flowers in their stems and halted his ambitions in that direction.

In all his life, he had never seen such flowers and he quickly asked out aloud, "*Magie gin maua machalnade?*" (What kind of flowers are these?) It was then that Nyar Nam told him that these were rose flowers, and that they had never been seen in this part of the land before except for today.

Oh yes! This was the first time ever, that the rose flower sprung up and dotted the *"flora"* or vegetation of the land, as well as blessing it with its immpecable ambience and spectacular beauty untold.

Being a farmer and a farmer also of great repute, it took Nyamgondho a good while to internalize that such captivating vegetation really existed and was now in his presence. It was true that the more he marvelled at the site of these flowers, the more he became obsessed with having Nyar Nam back in his homestead together with his *"mwandu"* (wealth).

It was while harboring or romancing with such thoughts and embraccing ideas in that direction, that all of a sudden, he heard a loud but firm heavily masculine voice emanating from the water, and it was around the same location as that of wich the old man with a tall walking stick that had disappeared upon his arrival stood. He quickly looked up towards that direction thinking that he could or would see him, but only more mystries was he to see or experience!

"Iwinjo omera." (Young man, are you listening?). The voice started to talk. *"Wuora ema oora kae mondo ati tije."* (My Father has sent me here to do His job). *"Nikech iye owang' kodi kabisa"* (Because he is very angry with you). *"Iparo ni koro aonge kae nikech ok inena."* (You think that I am not here because you are not seeing me).

The voice continued to talk. *"Ok inena nikwop koro aselokora yamo."* (You do not see me because now I have turned myself into air). *"Bende sechemoko an e mach maliet ma weng'o kendo ma ok ng'ire tir ka chieng minenono."* (And sometimes, I am the fire that you see burning and hard to look at straight in the eye like the sun that you see or know of).

"Kata samoro, alokora pi mange'ny mamol alanda kendo gudore kaka nam matut ma inenoni." (And sometimes also, I turn into large amounts of water that travel in floods, and later on settle in a deep lake that you see in front of you).

"E lak seche ma inenacha, oyudo ka akawo kit dhano nikech adwaro loso kodi matin kuom masira moyudi kawuononi." (At that very moment that you so me, I had assumed the body of a human being because I want to talk to you a little bit, concerning the misfortune that has befallen you today).

"Richoni ema omiyo mirima ogoya ngoga ma ochuna ni nyaka to alor mondo achul kuor ne ayany ma ne ibayone Nyar Nam cha." (Your sins have attracted my wrath in a very heavy fashion that it has forced me to revenge on behalf of Nyar Nam, especially concerning the insult that you hurled at her." The Voice continued, *"Eh, an ok chika to an ema achiko ji."* (Oh Yes! I am not instructed, but I am the one who instructs people).

"Iwinjo nyathina," (Hear me my son,), The Voice said in a very loving but serious tone. *"Ngima en midhiero."* (Life is a mystery). He paused for a while and added, *"Hera bende en mana midhiero ma ka ok idembo mana ka tong', to ogoyore piny kendo otoyore."* (Love is also a mystery that if you do not treat with the same delicacy of an egg, it falls down and cracks."

"To kotoyore mar adieri, to en toruok ma iwuoro ahinya, kendo onyalo kelo neko." (And if it fully cracks, the event becomes very historic indeed, that it can induce psychosis). *"Hera en gima idembo ka tong'."* (Love is treated with the delicacy of an egg).

He stopped again for a while but this time, the pause was a little bit longer and it seemed that He did this for a unique purpose. He then continued, *"Carelessness ok dwar e hera kata matin."* (Carelessness should be avoided at all costs in any

254

marriage). He then made it clear that, *"Iyudo masirani kawuono nikech carelessness mari."* (This misfortune befell you today because of your carelessness).

The Voice continued, *"Ne ichando mwandu ndalo mathoth kabisa, kendo kane isaya gi asaye mar adieri kendo malit ahinya, to ne awinjo lembi ma amiyi, kendo ne amiyi kaka idwaro."* (You lacked wealth and walloed in the quagmire poverty for a very long time, and when you sincerely prayed unto me, and painfully begged me to bless you with wealth, I heard your prayers and granted your wish, and as you wanted).

Upon recollecting this past, The Voice questioned, *"Ariambo koso awacho adieri?"* (Is this true or false?), and Nyamgondho quickly replied, *"Iwacho adieri."* (You are saying the truth).

The Voice continued, "Kuom gik ma otimore e ngimani kawuono nyaka itundo kae, donge koro iyie ni kaka ibam koda, e kaka an bende anabam kodi, mana kaka Nyar Nam ne puonjiga?" (With all that has happened to you today till right now, Don't you now agree that in as much as you are crooked with me in your ways, then I will also be crooked with you in my ways as Nyar Nam often counseled you?).

With a lot of shame and embarrassment engulfing him, Nyamgondho softly replied, *"Ayie mar adieri."* (I honestly and completely agree). Interestlingly enough, all this time, *"Nyamgondho ne osirore mana e ludhe mar kwath, ma kata go chonge piny ne ok ogoyo kata matin kaka joma sayo ng'uono mar adieri e masira makamae jotimoga."* (Nyamgondho kept on standing while leaning on his shepherd stick, and even kneeling down in the presence of the authority or the one of whom he intended to seek assistance from as was expected amongst people faced with such calamities, was not part of his plan or tradition at all).

The Voice continued, *"Chon, yande in ng'ama long'o kendo ratiro kabisa."* (A long time ago, you were an upright man and full of virtue).

"To tok yudo mwandu mag piny, ne ichako bayo njong' kabisa ka itimo timbe ma yore yore, timbe ma yombe, timbe mag anjao, kod timbe mag anyoso, kod timbe ma kwero makuodo wich kabisa, kendo kelo kuong' mager ei anyuola." (But once you started to ammerse earthly wealth, you began to indulge in filthy and shameful behaviour full of abominationable acts that attract deadly curses into the family lineage).

Nyamgondho could not lift his head up to face the direction of The Voice as these accusations were all true without any trace of a lie or bias towards Nyar Nam.

The Voice added, "*To, ne amiyi ndalo mang'eny mondo ilokri iduogi e wang' yo maler, to itamori kendo igur e richo mana ka ruoth mogur e kombe ma dak maye makata otho.*" (And I gave you a lot of time to turn back from your deviant ways and reform, but you refused and stuck in sin like a king who gets stuck to his throne that no one can take away from him even unto death).

Even though the conversational atmosphere was relatively pensive, the tension in the air could not be ignored especially when The Voice continued with the conversation saying, "*Ndalo mang'eny bende, Nyar Nam ne neno ka wasiki kod jomaundu obutoni kendo dwaro monji, to in idino iti kendo pod idhi ka bayo, chode, goch, mer kod bayo ayenje madongo dongo ne ji e gweng'.*" (Also, on several occassions, Nyar Nam detected that your enemies as well as robbers alike, were plotting against you and planning to harm you, but you gave a deaf ear to these alarms, and continued in your ways of demonstrating to the world your loose morals, alcoholic nature, catching fights with people, indulging in abominationations as well as hurling insults to people in the village).

All this time Nyamgondho was looking down at his *"tielo"* (feet) while listening as he knew that he had no strong defense if any. The Voice then asked Nyamgondho a question, "To koro, nikwayo mwandu kendo malit kabisa ma omiyi. To koro itimogodo ang'o maber?" (And now, you asked for weath very painfully, and you were given. As of now, is there any good that you have done with it?).

The Voice continued regrettingly asking him, *"Kata mana goyo erokamano ne ng'ama ne omiyi mwanduno bendo itimo?"* (Have you even thanked or showed appreciation to whoever gave you that wealth?) There was another noticeable moment of silence and as Nyamgondho thought that the Voice would continue speaking, he realized that the Voice was sincerely waiting for his response on this one.

It was then that Nyamgondho quickly responding by acknowledging that he had actually not done anything noble worth noting with his wealth, and neither has he shown any appreciation to the one who gave him access to the wealth that he craved for.

It was then that The Voice resumed his part of the conversation and proceeded by saying, *"To koro, nikwop idwaro chwanyo chuny Nyar Nam kendo gi chulo kwor ma isechanono, koro to ok anamiyigo kata matin."* (And now that you want to stir up the anger of Nyar Nam again with the revenge that you have planned, I am no longer going to give her to you at all).

The Voice continued in a very firm, assured and kingly or royalty-like tone saying, *"Bende ok abiyie mondo idog e dalani, nikwop, ji mang'eny nyalo tho kuom kwor ma isechano e chunyi ni mondo ichulno."* (And, I will also not allow you to go back to your home, because, many people can die due to the revenge that you have planned to carry out in your heart."

The fright in Nyamgondho, became more apparent as it had intesified especially when The Voice made it clear unto him that he was not going to go back to his homestead again. While he was shocked and in loss of words to even exclaim or talk back, Nyamgondho wondered how just a Voice of a Spirit, was going to be able to pin him down by the lakeside; And, if this was going to happen, did it mean tht he was going to die here?

"Eh." (Oh Yes.) The Voice continued and acknowledged that, *"Ang'eyo ni achwadi matek kendo malit kabisa, nikech, in iwuon, ing'eyo ni hera mar adieri en kido kod timbe, kendo, hera ok dwar mare kende kaka Nyar Nam nopwonji nyadi mang'eny to ichayo*

wechego." (I know that I have purnished you severely and very painfully, because, you personally know that true love is character and deeds; And that, love does not want only for itself as Nyar Nam had taught you several times ago, but you disrespected those words and took such teachings as things of nought.)

"De bed ni ionge gi kido mar chulo kwor e adundoni, to de aweyi idok ichak manyien, lakini wach chulo kuor mosiko e korini, ema omiyo bura koro oseloyi." (Had it not been for your character of revenge, I would have pardoned you, but because the issue of revenging is still very full and rife in your heart or bossom, the case before you, cannot be won by you.)

The Voice contined in a very authoritative manner saying, *"Koro, mana e tie nam kae, kama ichung'ieno, ema an bende ne aweyi kendo ne amiyi kuong' mara maduong' miwuoro mapok one e pinynie."* (Now, just at the shoes of this lake, where you have set your feet, is the location in which I will leave you in or affix you at, as I spell on you a curse that has never been known before in this land.)

It was clear that the sentiments of The Voice, had left a lot of pain, anguish or wrath on Nyamgondho that he was not finding it easy to even speak or utter any meaningful response on his matter.

The Voice, made it clear that, "*Chakre kawuono,*" (From today henceforth,), "*Ogendni duto te manie e piny mangima*", (All people from all walks of life around the world), "*Ne bi mondo oneni mana kanyo kanyo kaka ichung'no,*" (Will come to see you or view your image just there where you are curently standing on).

With increased or elated level of seriousness, The Voice added, "Ogendnigo birotimo kanamo ka giparogodo chwat malit kod wichkuot ma nyalo donjo ne dhano ka ochayo wang' Nyasache kendo wang' ng'etne kata jaode." (These multitudes of people from around the world, will come to see your body or remains, as they remember the shameful as well as the very painful curses that one can attract unto themselves whenever they disrespect their God as well as their spouse or loved one).

"*Eh!*" (Oh Yes!) "*Piny mangima ne nge niya, hera en midhiero matut ma ngero mare ong'e mana gi ji achiel ka achiel e mieche manitiere.*" (The entire world will know that, love is a very deep mystery whose parable is known or understood by only a handful of people in the communities of people that exist).

"Kendo, ne ging'e niya, ka ng'ato osedonjo e keny kata mana kend mar adieri, en kwero mang'ongo kabisa kuom sando ng'et mari kata jaodi kata nyithindi bende." (They will also know that, when someone has entered into a marriage relationshiop, it is an abominable act to abuse your spouse and even your children or offspiring).

"Gimaduong' e hera kae, en ni iher dhano wadu kaka in bende iherori iwuon, ka isiko iketo e pachi ni hera ok dwar mare kende" (What is of paramount importance in love, is that you should love your fellow human being as you love yourself, and always bearing in mind that love does not want only for itself).

"Gikanyono, Nyamgondho ne opo ka tiendege ochako bedo mang'ich moloyo kaka osewinjo e ngimane duto!" (At that very moment, Nyamgondo suddenly felt his feet beginning to get much colder than what he had ever experienced in all his life or entire life upto now!).

"To kane ong'iyo tiendene, to ne oneno ka tiendege osechako lokore yien kendo yien no, ne ochako two ka oneno gi wang'e kamae e wang' lela!". (And when he looked at his legs, he so that all his legs had started to turn into wood, and as he continued to look at them, the wood had started to dry in front of his very

own eyes, and in a way that anyone witnessing the scene could not deny!)

Chapter 24

*W*ith tears rolling down his eyes, there was now no doubt at all in his mind that he was *"bidding adieu"* to the things of this world or actually *"tho"* (dying) while literally standing and leaning on his *"luth mar kwath"* (shepherd's rod or stick) *"e wang' lela"* (in front of everybody) even as she had shamed and embarassed Nyar Nam earlier on.

It was then that Nyamgondho painfully learnt that, *"Hera mar adieri, en midhiero matut ahinya ma tek ng'eyo."* (True love is a mystery so deep that is not easy to understand or comprehend).

"To ka iyude, to onego ing'e ni hera ok dwar mare kende" (And when you find it, always remember that love does not want only for itself."

In fact, it is true that, *"Gima na Nyamgondho owacho gi chunye mogik, en ni ne oyie gi Nyar Nam kuom puonj mane opuonje chon ka owachoniya, hera ok dwar mare kende".* (The last words that Nyamgondho silently spoke to himself in his heart and mind, are the long-ago teachings of Nyar Nam in which she taught him that true love does not want only for itself).

For some reason. he felt the presence or the countenance of The Voice leaving him or withdrawing away from him.

The suffocating, terrible and nauseating feeling in his body at that time, was another confirmation that his life had come to an end; And, as he gradually became lonely, he quickly looked at the side in which he had seen Nyar Nam last, but was also in shock as Nyar Nam had quickly drifted into the wide expanse of the crocodile-infested lake and it appeared that the the rose flowers that he had seen earlier, were actually her boat that was literally carrying her to wherever she was going to in the lake, yet looking like rose flowers of impeccable beauty planted in the lake like fresh roseflowers in a flower vase today.

While standing like a very powerful, no-nonsense and an unchallenged *"Ruoth Manyako"* (Queen) amidst a signature collection of miraculously-floating *"maua"* (rose flowers), she was now a good distance away from the *"tie nam"* (shores) of the lake but still visible to Nyamgondho; And, as he watched her for the last time, he still did not believe that he was actually dying, and wanted to ask Nyar Nam for another chance to be with her for the rest of his life, or at least go with her to the lake.

However, as he opened his mouth to shout out his thoughts to Nyar Nam, it was then that he suffered the last installment of a mysterious and unique paralysis that had suddenly gripped his body; And, as history would have it, his *"dhoge ne omoko ka oyawore mang'ongo"* (mouth stuck wide open).

In as much as he was now completely paralysed and just waiting to yield the ghost or die completely, Nyar Nam knew that he was still not yet dead, and could not only comprehend but also, discern truth from its very first principles.

And it was then that Nyar Nam said unto him in a very firm voice and an unforgatable tone that, *"An ok yanya kata matin"* (I am never insulted even the least), while also making sure that all the *"jogweng'"* (villagers) that had rushed to the scene could *"winjo"* (listen) or hear just like Nyamgondho did when he insulted her in her very own *"dala"* (homestead).

As she spoke those words, her movement over the *"nam"* (lake) was very smooth and headed away from the shores towards the farthest distance from Nyamgondho's *"tielo"* (feet), and this was happening while she was above the miraculous-filled spectacular group of roses.

And it was at this point that Rieko finally ended his narrative by saying, "*Nyar Nam ne odhi ma olal e chuny pi tir gi maua maneolokore kaka yie ma okwang' godo.*" (Nyar Nam continued in her sail on the calm waters of the Lake Sango, atop the miraculous fresh roses that had turned into a boat, till she disappeared into the very heart of the water body, and never to be seen again by Nyamgondho for ever.)

Shortly after her "*lal*" (disappearence), an "*otenga marateng'*" (black eagle), came and landed on top of Nyamgondho's "*wich*" (head), and it was like it was confirming whether he was still "*mangima kata motho*" (alive or not).

And watching by the behavior of the "*otenga*" (eagle) as he not only swooped over his head, but also danced around his body in a very signature maneuver, it was apparent that "*chuny' Nyamgondho ne oweye*" (Nyamgondho's spirit had finally slipped away from his body) and he was officially no more.

It was then that the "*otenga*" (eagle) also flew away inching towards the sky, and ascending further and further into the boisterous clouds in great or terrific speeds.

267

Almost immediately, the whole *"chokruok"* (crowd) listening to this narrative, sprung up from their *"kombe"* (seats) and gave Rieko a thundering and well-deserved thunderous applause for his impeccable job that stood out as nothing but excellent, especially given the fact that his great grandfather's language was a second language to him or not his vernacular so to speak.

Even though the Luo language was not his vernacular or mother-tongue, he defied the odds and learnt it anyway, and through *"tich matek"* (hardwork), *"horuok"* (patience), and *"kinda mathoth"* (sheer determination), he had gone above and beyond in acquiring its matery as well as using it skillfully to convey or relay a profound message and now, he was just waiting for that new, one-of-a-kind thriller and first-time-to-be-heard-of *"sigana"* (narrative) of Chief Leinad Ongoda.

Chapter 25

*C*hief Leinad Ongoda gave him a pat on the back and thanked him immensely for saving the situation that he had at hand. He was still battling with *"olo kod jony'"* (fatigue) and lack of enough sleep, and he knew that it a few moments, he would be ready to narrate unto them the new *"sigana"* (story) in his mind.

Of particular importance also, were the profound and much-needed lessons that Chief Leinad Ongoda wanted to teach *"langi mare"* (members of his lineage), as well as the value system that he favored for them to adopt, or live by even as a code of conduct or foundation of ethics, principles and morals that enabled one to live peacefully with one another in the *"gwenge"* (communities) that they found themselves in even if they be foreign or distant.

This value system, is a value system that embraced the tradition or adopted the culture of trying to leave peacefully with one another even if they appear to be different from you physically, or even if they are of a different school of thought, origin or in whatever one felt important or valuable to them.

Chief Leinad Ongoda knew the treasure or the golden nuggets that were hidden in this value system as he was a great beneficiary of defending peace even in environments where the *"kodhi mag kwe"* (seeds of peace) did not have a promising area or season to grow, especially with him being an immigrant in a foreign country full of people with sometimes strikingly opposing views of the same thing.

In fact, Chief Leinad Ongoda even shared with his grandchildren and great grandchildren alike, his personal experiences in which he found social stereotypes and racial profiling to be a limiting factor to many who were practicing them not only at *"kwonde tich"* (work places), but also in other environments or *"aluora"* (social settings) worth noting.

While in his undergraduate years at a very reputable university that was also famed for the beauty of its main campus and inspiring it to be known around the world as "The Campus Beautiful", and located in the most powerful country in the world, Chief Leinad Ongoda noticed a very important aspect of human nature that often came from experience but was worth knowing beforehand lest one judge their fellow man wrongly and attract unto them wrath or *"masira"* (attrocities) that could have otherwise been avoided or dealt with differently.

While pursuing his undergraduate degree there at Concord University in Athens, West Virginia, United States of America (USA), Chief Leinad Ongoda told his children and grand children alike, his true experience on race especially due to the fact that he was a black man, and of an international descent or origin and heritage, and attending college in a predominantly white university or institution of higher learning.

It was taken by many almost for granted that all *"abonyo, jorochere or msungu"* (white people) were racist or "red-necks" as they were popularly known, and especially if they looked like a specific kind of white people who were believed to be much more racist than others, and even inspired the "coining" of the phrase "red-necks" .

But having lived and studied, and even worked with *"jorochere"* (white people), attended *"kanisa"* (church) with them, shopped with them in the same malls or shopping centers and generally lived with them, I testify that the stereotypes of "red-necks" or racist just due to color alone, is a lie, and quite a damaging lie it is indeed.

It is my true, solemn and sincere testimony that there are many white people who are sincerely not only God-fearing and rooted in the Gospel as per the biblical standards upheld in the society, but are also at the fore-front of promoting a true and genuine brotherly love for one another in their respective communities irrespective of skin color, tribal background or ethnicity, nationality or country of origin, religious belief or other controversial social orientations.

Chief Leinad Ongoda made it clear to his children and great grandchildren alike, therefore to tread cautiously with stereotypes whenever it came up to or popped up in their relationships with other people, and to always see another person as a child of God Most High who truly and sincerely deserves equal love and respect that they would also like to be given or accorded at all times and in all places they may find themselves in.

This should be true even if it is in an *"od twech or jela"* (prison-setting) as sometimes, in our *"wuodhwa e piny ma mwalo kae"* (journey in this fallen and troubled world), one can find themselves as being *"ng'atma omakne bura ma miriambo"* (accused wrongly), or find themselves imprisoned or jailed without a fair *"trial"* (trial).

Also, amongst the many things that Chief Leinad Ongoda noticed that his *"mbesene"* (peers) or parents in geneneral, *"ne ok otimo kare"* (did not do correctly) or pay much attention to, was the dire need to observe parental guidance ratings especially to the content or information, or material that their children had access to, especially when they were under the age of thirteen years.

This was why in as much as the story of Nyamgondho was more than what he shared with his children and grandchildren and great grandchildren alike, he hid from them some parts of the story in respect of their age and their need to mature up in a respectable environment that did not expose them to adult-rated material or content until they were ready for them, and expressed a desire to access them or even appreciate them.

However, it suffices to say that in so far as those things or ideas, or teachings that were related to belief systems, religion or faith-based truths or information, Chief Leinad Ongoda often mentioned *"weche matek"* (tough-to-understand information) just in passing, for the purposes of inspiring the much-needed and always-important research and development aspect in one's life.

One of those profound *"puonjruok"* (teachings) that Chief Leinad Ongoda knew very well and internalized not only just as a responsible person or individual in the society, but also as a world-renowned or internationally-reputed *"jakoro or janabi"* (Seer or Prophet), was that life in this mortal world or firmament, or in this sanguine planet, did not begin here as we know it, neither does it end here as some people like Nyamgondho thought even when they had an abundance of opportinities to think otherwise especially for their own safety or security not only in the world or material space that they lived in, but also in immortality.

Chief Leinad Ongoda knew very well and taught the interested people that, the gospel of pre-mortality was not a myth at all, as it was revealed to him very vividly and several times in a number of heavenly *"fwenje"* (visions) by non other than *Ramogi Ajwang'* Himself, of whom he prophesized for, and by His unwavering as well as unchallenged authority and divine power.

Chief Leinad Ongoda also knew and taught the interested people that, the *"piny mokwongo"* (first world) that man ever experiences or "*dak e iye*" (lives in) straight from "*polo*" (heaven) is the world of the "*ich min*" (womb), and that their experiences in that world, is lost by many when they enter the life on this sanguine planet right after "*nywolruok margi*" (their birth); And hence, making life on this planet as life in the "*piny mar ariyo ma ok en piny mokwongo*" (second and not the first world).

Chief Leinad Ongoda also knew and taught the interested people that, the next world after life on this planet, was life in a place that some people called purgatory, and it was a very painful life indeed for they who sinned and failed to make it back to heaven, but were fortunate enough to be given another chance to repent of their sins even though it was not a probationary place like in this planet.

Chief Leinad Ongoda also knew that some of his great grandchildren were not aware that he was also known or referred to by other names by many from other "*pinje*" (worlds or continents), especially those who knew him as a "*Jakoro mang'ongo ahinya*" (a great prophet), as he also had the ability to even successfully "*lemo ne chunje mosetho machando jomangima*" (pray for the fallen spirits of the dead that troubled or tormented the living), as they were trapped in the various painful-to-live parts of purgatory, and were in dire need for "yweyo e polo" (rest in heaven).

Also, being a *"Jakoro Mang'ongo ahinya"* (a great prophet), Chief Leinad Ongoda exhorted especially his children, great grandchildren, great great grandchildren and many others, of the value of being on the right side of, or walking in the favor of *Ramogi Ajwang'* (God of their ancestors also known by other names in other cultures), lest they suffer a similar fate as Nyamgondho in their lives; And, amongst the neccessary and unchallenged requisites of winning the favor of *Ramogi Ajwang'*, was the*"kwedo mar richo"* (hate for sin). or avioding in engaging in *"timbe maricho"* (bad habits).

Amongst the *"richo"* (sins) or *"timbe maricho"* (bad habits) that Chief Leinad Ongoda could mention from the top of his head, were: *"terruok"* (adultery), *"tim ma ok ler"* (fornication), *"anjawo"* (uncleanness), *"chode"* (lasciviousness), *"lamo nyiseche manono"* (idolatry), *"jwok"* (witchcraft), *"sigu"* (hatred), *"dhaw"* (variance), *"nyiego"* (emulations), *"mirima"* (wrath), *"ichlit"* (strife), *"miero"* (seditions), *"pogruok e kanyakla"* (heresies), *"gombo"* (envyings), *"neko"* (murders), *"mer"* (drunkenness), *"budho mok kare"* (revellings), and many other similar sinful acts.

Chief Leinad Ongoda also testified unto them that if one would successfully avoid these sinful acts in their own or personal lives, then they will be blessed by the Almighty with the much-needed and uniquely precious fruits of The Spirit of God Almighty Himself; And these included: *"True Love"* (Hera mar adieri), *"mor"* (joy), *"kue"* (peace), *"horuok"* (longsuffering), *"ng'wono"* (gentleness), *"ber"* (goodness), *"bedo ja adiera"* (faith), *"muolo"* (meekness), *"ritruok"* (temperance), and it was true that against such fruits of The Spirit of God, there is no law at all.

It was also true that, for they like Chief Leinad Ongoda who had been spiritually gifted enough as to seeing *Ramogi Ajwang'* Himself, and by His divine power, as a *"Jakoro mare"* (His prophet), could attest that among'st His *"Osimbo kata ogudu mare mar ng'ongo kod loch ma wasungu kata odiero dendo ni crown, chal mana kaka ligeke mag mach mager ahinya, ma ok rwakre ne ng'ato ang'ata mak mana ka en owuon, ema orwakone kaka jaote mare moro."* (His crown or heard-gear that symbolized His royal authority as well as His unchallenged leadership, looked like blazing tongues of fire that no one could put on, wear or adorn unless He Himself adorned such attire on His divine messengers or emmisaries of some kind or sort).

Even though his great grandchildren had not yet matured enough to handle some *"sigana"* (stories) of faith that were inspiried by *"adieri mane otimore"* (true occurences), Chief Leinad Ongoda made it clear to them that there were many tales especially from their *"kwere"* (ancestry) that warned many of the dire consequences from Ramogi Ajwang' Himself, of one pretending to be a *"jakoro or janabi"* (Seer or Prophet), yet they were not, like the story of a one infamous man in the Luoland named as or called Origa.

In as much as the story of Origa was a story of another day, it was important to mention that when Origa, who was once a true and sincere follower of Ramogi Ajwang', but due to his *"gombo maricho"* (ill-concieved as well as ill-inspired ambitions), coupled with spiritual corruption in high places, and the love for making money in the *"hekalu"* (church), was tempted one day to secretly put on the *"Ogudu mar ng'ongo kod dolo"* (crown of authority and priesthood) of *Ramogi Ajwang'* also known by many others as Baba Messiah Himself, and upon doing so, was later on identified as a *"Jakoro ma miriambo"* (false prophet) by they who later on, found out what he had done as he had no holy annointing of Baba Messiah with him.

"Origa ne oyudo chwat mang'ongo sana kuom pimo ogudu mar Baba Messiah, kendo bang' mano ne oyudo sandruok malit kabisa nyaka e chuny mach tir bang' ka osetho, ma onge lemo moro amora manenyalo gole kuno." (Subsequently, Origa attracted unto himself the servere wrath of God for his sinful action, and after that incident, his life was full of a myryad of torments or painful experiences untold, even unto death; And after death in hell, such that there were no prayers up to today, that can give him any relief wherever he is in hell, or remove him out of hell, or from the unmerciful and fierce fires of real hell altogether).

The Great Ramogi Ajwang' much later, revealed to Chief Leinad Ongoda in person that, *"Origa bende ne mer ga mana ka Nyamgondho ka otimo timbegi, kendo ne orwako crown mara ma matakatifu, ka oserogodo nyi kanisa, kendo olombo godo chwo wetegi e donjoe timbe mag kwero kabisa ma itimo mana e chuny mudho tir."* (Origa was also a regular consumer of alcohol just like Nyamgondho whenever he engaged in such sacrilageous acts, and he put on My Holy Crown for the purposes of seducing the women in the church, as well as attracting unto himself his male counterparts or colleagues for the purposes of engaging in abominations or deeply sinful and sacrilageous acts that were often done or commited in the deepest or darkest hours of dark nights).

Anyway, a couple of minutes had passed since Rieko completed his narrative and even before Rieko could sit down, hands shot up, and this time several hands were already in the air for another one to narrate his "sigana" (story).

It was clear that all of them were looking for some attention even as Rieko got for his job well done. There was some competition here and Chief could not ignore this need even though he was ready to narrate the story of the season.

As he looked at all of them, one of his great grandchildren called Ogwedhi had been humble for a long time and was the first one to put up his hand for selection to narrate his "*sigana*" (story) before all others yet he did not attract his attention by making noise or fidgeting, rather he attracted attention by his humble silence and it was him that Chief Leinad Ongoda pointed at.

While focusing his attention on Ogwedhi, there was something striking or rather unique about his character as well as the talents that he had already show-cased unto all of them including his siblings. It was his talents in art that defined him even more than any other gifts or academic ability, or even the intellectal prowess or ability exhibited in school.

This aspect of him reminded Chief Leinad Ongoda of some of the frustrations that he experienced in his youthful days while going through primary and secondary school or grade school, especially in a family in which his father was not only a High School teacher of Mathematics and Physics, but also a High School Principal famed for his disciplinary method of not sparing the cane to spoil the child, as well as laying more emphasis on the study and exhibiting of great proficiency in Mathematics and Physics, while not giving that much priority, attention or importance to other subjects or disciplines being taught in school as part of the entire school curriculum.

In fact, Chief Leinad Ongoda could remember many times in high school whenever he moved to a new grade, his father would only buy for them Mathematics and Physics textbooks first while dragging his feet or attempting to ignore the need of purchasing for them the *"buge"* (textbooks) required for other subjects or courses.

Being a person who was a self-learner, his father's behaviour and *"achaye"* (negative attitude) towards the study of arts, humanities and languages, really made him angry or annoyed him, but he could not challenge the authority of his father or his opinion, or even reason with him on this matter as he was not even that kind of person to be approached in that nature.

Several times, Chief Leinad Ongoda told his children and other descendants about his father reminding them that, *"Wuonwa ne en ng'ama ger ka pino ma ka itugo, to onyalo kayi ma ihinyri kabisa."* (Our father's anger was that which could be compared to the wrath of honnets that if provoked, could cause serious pain as well as unforgettable injuries).

However, in as much as this was the environment in which he grew up in, while skillfully managing to satisfy and even exceed the expectations of his parents as well as the community on his performance, and even successfully establishing a career in a Math-oriented as well as a science-oriented field with lustruous success, deep down in his heart, he always knew and made sure that he never suppressed or ignored his creative nature as he always had an "eye for the arts" and and "ear for the languages" so to speak.

In fact, upon settling himself in a *"tich ma omi luor"* (descent career), he made a sincere committment with himself to try as much as possible to promote the arts and talented individuals who were either misunderstood, stereotyped, given lower priority in inclusion in the academic circles, denied funding for the promotion of their art or natural gifts or talents, and even abandoned all together by both family and their society as well.

One day, while actively engaging in his *"sombe owuon"* (personal studies) in the pursuit of the Arts in his *"thuolo mare ma kende"* (free time), he rejoiced when he came across or found a quote that he concurred with or attested to; And, the quote was from a seasoned and well respected artist who made it clear unto the entire world that, "Artists are the gatekeeper of truth in the society, and if their voices are silenced, then a whole or an entire civilization, irrespective of its greatness, or the largeness of its expanse, will begin to crumble and even perish as history has proven over and over again in different ages, eras or epochs, or other significant time-frames of time worth noting."

It was mainly due to this reason that he did not hesitate to hold back Ogwedhi from show-casing his talent and being the best he was in a very comfortable, supporting and welcoming environment of his family.

However, as he pointed at him to narrate his story, through his natural body language, Chief Leinad Ongoda made it clear that this time round, the narratives should be "*machieko*" (relatively short) and quick to the point as time was of the essense.

Upon being chosen to be the next center of attraction in this "*budho*" (gathering), while clearing his voice loudly, Ogwedhi sprung up from where he was seated, and with the swiftness of a deer as well as the agility of a dove, he quickly dashed to the stage in preparation for his much-awaited narrative.

End of Series I.

Milton Keynes UK
Ingram Content Group UK Ltd.
UKHW010709040923
428018UK00014B/952